GOVERNMENT IN SCIENCE

GOVERNMENT IN SCIENCE

The U.S. Geological Survey
1867-1894

Thomas G. Manning

UNIVERSITY OF KENTUCKY PRESS

TO THE MEMORY OF
MY FATHER AND MOTHER
Arthur and Gertrude Manning

ACKNOWLEDGMENTS

I am under heavy obligation to historians, scientists, and other professional people. An acceptable manuscript could never have been presented for publication without their assistance, which was so freely given. I have tried to remember all whose knowledge and advice were drawn upon, and I hope that I have not forgotten anyone. First there are the historians: Samuel Flagg Bemis, Harold Dean Cater, William Culp Darrah, Hunter Dupree, Francis P. Farquhar, Bob Ferrell, Ralph Gabriel, Bill Goetzmann, John Higham, Oliver W. Holmes, Tom LeDuc, Dick Lowitt, Ed Lurie, Otis Marston, Stow Persons, George Pierson, David Potter, J. Eugene Smith, Wallace Stegner, and M. M. Vance. Then come the scientists: Henry R. Aldrich, H. M. Bannerman, Bob Beringer, W. H. Bradley, Richard Flint, the Adolph Knopfs, Chester Longwell, the late W. C. Mendenhall, Thomas B. Nolan, W. T. Pecora, John Rodgers, A. S. Romer, William W. Rubey, Julian Sears, Al Wade, and the late W. E. Wrather. At Texas Technological College, where the book was written, I consulted with Tod Baker, Sterling Fuller, Larry Graves, Alan Gunn, Keneth Kinnamon, J. T. McCullen, Otto Nelson, Ben Newcomb, Alan Strout, Idris Traylor, and David Welborn. Several others should certainly be recognized: Mrs. George F. Becker, Carroll Bowen, Agnes Creagh, Marjorie Downing, Frank Forrester, David Horne, Savoie Lottinville, Mrs. George P. Merrill, and Sidney S. Walcott.

The American Council of Learned Societies, the Geological Society of America, and the Department of History, Yale University, helped me financially. The Library of Congress, the library of the U. S. Geological Survey, the National Archives, the Sterling Memorial Library, the Peabody Museum of Natural History, and the library at Texas Technological College were the major locations for my research. I was well received at all these places. Other institutions which made my work easier were: the Minnesota Historical Society, the State Historical Society in Wisconsin, the Nevada State Historical Society, the Michigan State Historical Society, the Hayes Memorial Library, the Huntington Library, the American Museum of Natural History, the Museum of Comparative Zoology at Harvard College, the Hartford Public High School, Illinois College, the Milner Library at Illinois State Normal University, and the University of Rochester library. For secretarial services I remember Anne O'Neal, Jeanette Stewart, the late Katherine Barnes, Mrs. Syrian E. Marbut, and Jane Rodman. Mrs. Bob Parker of Lubbock, Texas, typed the final manuscript. Ellis Buckner, also of Lubbock, consented to read galley and page proof with me.

I am indebted to the U. S. Geological Survey for the four maps in this book. Bob Moravetz and Melvin Hanes of the Publications Division in Washington asked Jack Hopkins of the Survey office in Lexington, Kentucky, to arrange for the drafting of these maps.

CONTENTS

MAPS

INTRODUCTION

The history of the United States Geological Survey concerns knowledge and research, how they developed, and how they were involved in legislation and politics during the latter part of the nineteenth century. The origins of the Survey date from the period after 1865 when the federal government became more important than the states in sponsoring the study of geology, paleontology, and topography. Scientific surveys operating in the trans-Mississippi West did the research, and they introduced almost every program which later was prominent in the Geological Survey proper.

The pattern of the research and the returns from it are primary themes in this history. The Survey and the explorations in the West which preceded it exploited the new field of physical geology, which was almost an American innovation. Clarence King, the Survey's first director, established a continuous and effective connection with the mining industry through economic geology. Under the directorship of John Wesley Powell, the Survey accumulated topographical knowledge at a rapid pace, through plans for a national map. Advances also were made in vertebrate and invertebrate paleontology. Theorizing flourished as knowledge developed and its emphasis shifted. Scientists sought to explain the origin of ore deposits, to define the stages of erosion, and to understand the equilibrium of the geological strata on the earth's surface. The great theoretical issue of geoscience in the last quarter of the nineteenth century was the rate of physical change in geological time, and geologists of the Survey supported the idea of uniform change on the earth's surface, past and present. They also speculated about the proper balance between fact-gathering and theorizing in the method of competent scientists.

The Geological Survey was an impressive force in government science, because its research harmonized with general historical trends of post-Civil War America—westward expansion, the rise of industry, the extension of federal power, and urbanization. The favorable position of the Survey in American history determined the nature of its politics, as periodically Congress felt drawn to investigate so new and so thriving a bureau. When the legislature intervened, it pressed against those segments of the Survey's research which scientists themselves had made controversial. The result was that the politicians either sanctioned the Survey work done or limited its activity by redesigning the research program. The first phase of this bureaucratic growth and congressional challenge reached a climax in 1879 when the U. S. Geological Survey was founded, 10 or 12 years after several geological surveys had been established in western territories. The competition between these surveys antagonized Congress, which, even as it organized the unified Survey, reduced the scope and cost of the science involved. At this time the issue was not simply the emphasis of the research or its extent, but there was also considerable disagreement about the person and group to control the new bureau. The Survey soon broke down the legislative restrictions of 1879. It came east across the Mississippi River in 1882, collaborated with the older states, and resumed most of the research which had been abandoned in 1879. Then in the mid-eighties came the reaction, now almost a forgotten chapter in the history of the bureau. Cleveland Democrats, inspired by a laissez-faire ideology, proposed a broad reduction in federal research, arguing it was inappropriate and too expensive. Some government science suffered, but the Survey was vindicated in all its policies since 1879. Even more important, the bureau was recognized as a permanent scientific establishment.

There was a widening application of Survey knowledge to American life at the end of the decade and into the nineties. Through activity which would be incongruous for the present-day Survey, geologists fought successfully for the integrity of Yellowstone Park. Then during a study of irrigation prospects beyond the one hundredth meridian, J. W. Powell, the second director, sought reform through scientific knowledge, as he tried to direct westward migration into a new type of community. The irrigation survey was the great disaster of the nineteenth-century bureau. Scientists were divided bitterly over the emphasis topographical knowledge should have in such a survey, and a score of western senators were offended deeply when the public land system was threatened with suspension, while the government classified the irrigable land. In 1892, after the demise of the irrigation studies, the western senators took their revenge, joining Cleveland supporters opposed to government science. Senators and representatives especially attacked Survey projects in paleontology. As a result, the bureau entered a brief period of decline.

The history of the nineteenth-century Geological Survey foreshadows the complex relationship between contemporary science and government. The early Survey presents political themes and topics which have continued into modern times. One of these enduring themes is the conflict between civilians and the military over control of science, dramatically illustrated during the controversy which accompanied the founding of the Survey in 1879. A second topic or problem common both in the past and the present is the scope of government science. In the late nineteenth century politicians and scientists continually tried to use the distinction between practical and theoretical knowledge as a basis for limiting public research to the practical. Another recurring problem is low quality science, which crept into the nineteenth-century Survey through partisan demands for patronage and scientists' thirst for glory. The legislative cry for economy influenced deeply the Survey's early history, and it is still an important factor in public science. Some scientists will always be fascinated by the social and ethical implications of newly discovered knowledge; the second director (Powell) precipitated a serious crisis by applying Survey research to reform action. Several chapters deal with the relationship of the Survey to the committee system of Congress, to legislative debates and to the power of the President and his personal attitude toward science. Of course these two branches of the government still speak decisively on the encouragement or control of natural knowledge. Ultimately the reader will judge for himself the contemporary significance of the nineteenth-century Survey. The past events may simply confirm some present-day experience of his own; or he may find in these bygone affairs inspiration for his own thinking and zeal concerning the future. Realizing the continuity of events, he loses a harmful sense of isolation. His problems are not uniquely difficult; the burden of history is shared.

Chapter One

FEDERAL SCIENCE IN THE
TRANS-MISSISSIPPI WEST AFTER 1865

The exploration and development of the American Far West, which proceeded rapidly following the end of the Civil War, encouraged the growth of geology and led to the founding of the United States Geological Survey. Geology as modern, organized knowledge originated during the nineteenth century, when many principles and techniques of the discipline were firmly established. At the very beginning of the century Abraham Gottlob Werner of Saxony demonstrated that rocky materials on the earth's surface often followed a regular order and could be systematically described. In France, Georges Cuvier, by bringing certainty and accuracy to the study of fossils, developed the allied science of paleontology. Then, William Smith of England used fossils extensively to distinguish rock strata and put them in order. In the 1830's a major strengthening for the science came when Sir Charles Lyell published his *Principles of Geology*. Lyell taught geologists how to approach past geological change; he advised studying the causes now in operation on the earth's surface and assuming that these causes operated similarly in the past.

Active and important research began for American geology in the 1830's and 1840's when the state surveys of New York and Pennsylvania were organized. The results in New York emphasized the Paleozoic or very ancient strata of the geological column; in Pennsylvania the fruitful topics were coal basins and the structure of the Appalachian mountain system. James D. Dana of Yale College established an independent American branch of the science when he published his celebrated textbook, *Manual of Geology,* in 1863. Dana focused attention on the North American continent and drew his illustrations of life mostly from the American scene. His scientific terminology exercised a powerful influence on the future, because the names in the *Manual* for the rock strata of the geological column provided a framework for decades of research in North American formations.

A promising field for this dynamic science was a mountain, plateau, and basin region of the Far West, comprising the state of Nevada and the territories of Colorado, Wyoming, Utah, and Arizona. Geologists knew that sedimentary rocks of the major geological systems were to be found in this large and distant area, for Dana's textbook carried facts from the reports of scientific explorations, but no real earth history on a regional scale had yet been attempted.

Public sentiment was favorable to scientific studies. The Pacific railroad project, well underway in the mid-sixties, demonstrated the intense interest of the American people in the trans-Mississippi West. To many of them the great interior was unknown or mysterious, and they approved broad searches in the name of knowledge to uncover wonders and riches. The mining industry had a direct stake in western geology. For its part the federal government already had agencies willing to undertake research in the territories. Among these was the War Department which practiced science in the tradition of two generations of army officers and engineers. They valued topography as the highest form of peacetime knowledge, and they were the architects of the authoritative map of the American West. These military engineers were also familiar with astronomy, geodesy, hydrography, and meteorology. Frequently, they invited civilian scientists to accompany them on western expeditions. As a consequence, most of the geologists who studied the American interior had served in War Department parties. Perhaps the climax of the War Department's geological effort came in 1859 when J. S. Newberry, observing the Grand Canyon while traveling in the party of Lieutenant J. C. Ives, a topographical engineer, concluded (correctly) that it had been formed by erosion and not by some convulsion of nature. The Department of the Interior, which directed ad hoc surveys to determine the agricultural or mineral resources of the public lands, was primarily interested in economic geology. The most successful of its surveys had come in the copper and iron ore region of the Great Lakes. After the Civil War there were hopes for similar work in the trans-Mississippi country; the General Land Office of the department arranged a display of precious and useful minerals from all the states and territories with the rock specimens identified according to Dana's terminology.[1] The Smithsonian Institution was another research center in Washington. In the science of western exploration it planned for observations and collections on its own, provided equipment, recommended staff, and gave advice to other surveys. It also studied the materials brought back.

The geologists who organized surveys to fit the opportunities of post-Civil War America were Clarence King, F. V. Hayden, and John Wesley Powell. These three raised the science of geology to new levels of accomplishment and independence within the federal government and thus prepared the way for the U. S. Geological Survey. Their work added to the permanent stock of geological knowledge and determined lines of future research. They advanced both theoretical and practical geology, and they made intensive studies and also regional explorations. No survey was without topography and paleontology, though the emphasis upon these other sciences varied enormously. Sometimes a peripheral subject dominated survey activity. Apart from their intrinsic merit, these variations are important because most of them reappeared in the U. S. Geological Survey. And such differences

[1] *Report of the Commissioner of the General Land Office for the Fiscal Year Ending June 30, 1868* (Washington, 1868), 120.

figured prominently in a movement toward consolidation, when the programs and personalities of the several surveys competed for preferential standing within a united bureau. The diversity extended to relations with the established order of government science, as each geologist moved in his own way to avoid subordination of himself or his knowledge. King, Hayden, and Powell exploited popular trends to advance their scientific and political interests. All three wanted to explore the West and direct settlement there, and each connected his work with some timely problem in mining or agriculture. In their success they expressed and recognized the forces of modern science, of the westward movement, and of the federal government (representing the American people), which were making geology a compelling field of knowledge.

Clarence King began the United States Geological Exploration of the Fortieth Parallel in 1867. His program for government science laid heavy emphasis upon utilitarian and even technological features. This emphasis had permanent consequences, for King gave it the central place in the U. S. Geological Survey, of which he became the first director. And long after his departure, these utilitarian features remained to strengthen the Geological Survey and assure its future.

Stimulated toward practical science by his education at Yale College, where he graduated in 1862, King decided to work with the mining industry, confident of its receptivity. Industry spokesmen were lamenting the ignorance and wastefulness of mining practice, and they petitioned the federal government asking for education or research efforts to improve efficiency. King offered to study the Comstock Lode at Virginia City, to visit other silver centers of Nevada, and to inspect mining in Colorado.[2] At the Comstock, the richest

2 See the letters of recommendation which King brought with him to Washington in 1867. Office of the Chief of Engineers, Letters Received,

of all American silver-gold lodes, he would explain the geology, the mechanics of underground exploration, and the methods of ore extraction and purification at the mills.

The Exploration of the Fortieth Parallel was also a personal quest for King. Dana's *Manual* had inspired him to become a geologist and to imitate his professor by writing "a piece of connected history."[3] After an overland journey in 1863 to join the California Geological Survey, he felt sure that the long stretch of territory across the Great Basin in Utah and Nevada, between the Middle Rocky Mountains and the Sierra Nevada, was the best location for such a study. To do this Great Basin history properly, King needed geological and topographical mapping, and he projected a zone for this mapping 100 miles wide. To gain legislative support, he promised that this zone would include the Union and Central Pacific lines. He and his senatorial friends, John Conness of California and William M. Stewart of Nevada, praised the transcontinental railroad as a good beginning in joining the populated Pacific coast with the East, thus strengthening the nation in time of civil crisis. But a line of mining communities narrowing the gap of uninhabited country would make the bonds of union even stronger, they said.[4] And King cleverly suggested that his extensive geological mapping would stimulate mineral discoveries, the foundation of such communities. After this promise, he could hardly avoid mapping along the railroads. But he gave only limited attention to economic topics there, reserving the intensive studies for already active mining centers in Nevada

---

1867, U. S. National Archives. Hereinafter cited as Chief of Engineers, Letters Received.

[3] Clarence King, *Systematic Geology* (Washington, 1878), 4. For King's conversion by Dana, see Clarence King to George J. Brush, January 30, 1863, Brush Family Papers, Yale University Library.

[4] *Clarence King Memoirs* (New York, 1904), 265. For a statement by Stewart, see U. S., *Congressional Globe*, 40th Cong., 2nd Sess., January 16, 1868, p. 560.

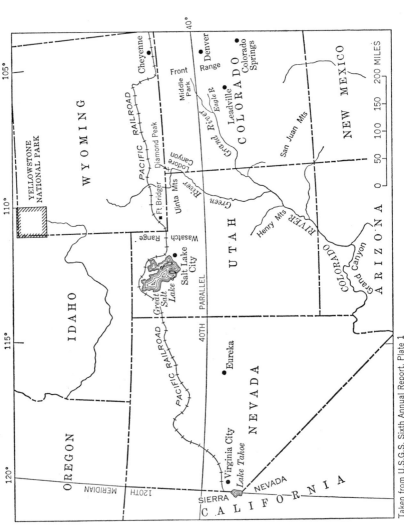

AREA OF THE WESTERN SURVEYS AFTER 1865

Taken from U.S.G.S. Sixth Annual Report, Plate 1

and Colorado. The argument for the Union was chiefly patriotic veneer to cover the sweeping project in pure science.

King proposed that his exploration become part of the Corps of Engineers, inheritors after the Civil War of the strong army and War Department position in the western territories. He also believed that if his plan was approved by the corps and the War Department, negotiations with Congress for an appropriation would be easier. Going to Washington in January 1867, he conferred with Secretary of War Edwin M. Stanton and General Andrew Atkinson Humphreys, chief of the corps.[5] His purpose in talking with Humphreys was to convince the general that he knew topography and geology and that he merited an independent field command. He furnished impressive letters of recommendation testifying to his versatility "in the higher branches of topographic surveying" and his skill with astronomical instruments.[6] Humphreys recommended King to Stanton, granted King autonomy by saying that he could report directly to the Office of the Chief of Engineers rather than to some subordinate administrator within the bureaucracy, and unexpectedly offered money from the "surveys of military defenses" fund.[7] Congressional permission should be secured, he said, to spend this money for a geological and topographical survey. Thus did the chief of the corps advance an uncertain cause. Colonel R. S. Williamson, the senior engineer officer on the Pacific coast, had been skeptical that Congress would grant even a small appropriation, and King was asking for $50,000 immediately. Supported by the War Department, he had only to justify his plan to several senators, and legislative approval

5 Thurman Wilkins, *Clarence King: A Biography* (New York, 1958), 94-95; "Geographical and Geological Surveys West of the Mississippi," U. S., House Report No. 612, 43rd Cong., 1st Sess., 83. Hereinafter cited as "Surveys West of the Mississippi."

6 See, particularly, R. S. Williamson to H. L. Abbot, November 3, 1866, Chief of Engineers, Letters Received, 1867.

7 A. A. Humphreys to E. M. Stanton, January 21, 1867, "Surveys West of the Mississippi," 84.

became a formality. No protesting voices were heard when on February 7, 1867, Senator John Conness of California moved to authorize the exploration along the route of the Pacific railroad on the condition that no new money be appropriated.

The working schedule demonstrated King's intention to stimulate the science and technology of western mining.[8] He made the preparation of a mining volume his first business, hiring engineer James D. Hague and sending him to the Comstock Lode at Virginia City, Nevada. The point of departure for the zonal geology also reflected the primary interest in economic geology. Instead of traveling westward by land to the Wyoming-Utah border, King went by sea to California and began mapping eastward into Nevada with the help of two geological assistants, Samuel Franklin Emmons and Arnold Hague (brother of James). This move gained early access to mineral areas, particularly to the Comstock Lode at Virginia City, where King and his aides joined James D. Hague for the winter of 1867-1868. The leader prepared a geological description of the district and an explanation of the structure of the silver-gold lode. James D. Hague studied mining and milling processes. In its first and perhaps most important phase, the Fortieth Parallel Exploration was a geological survey of Nevada.

Mining Industry, the first volume from King's investigations, appeared in 1870, years ahead of the purely geological volumes or the topographical atlases. Scientists praised James D. Hague, the chief author. *The American Journal of Science* approved his chapters on appliances and methods for digging and treating ores at the Comstock and commended his statistics on the amount and cost of ore production. Hague was

8 Clarence King to A. A. Humphreys, August 3, December 6, 18, 1867, March 5, August 13, November 14, 1868, August 26, 1869, February 14, 1871, U. S. Geological Exploration of the Fortieth Parallel, Letters to the Chief of Engineers, 1867-1878, U. S. National Archives.

responsible for "the most valuable contribution yet made to the literature of the Mining Industry of the United States."[9] Ten years later John A. Church, professor of mining at Ohio State University, reaffirmed this opinion of *Mining Industry*; it was never likely to lose its prominence and value, he said.[10] Scientists also recognized King's additions to the geological knowledge of the Comstock district. The miners had made more openings into the lode since the time of his distinguished predecessor, Baron von Richthofen, and thus he was able to give a fuller description of the rocks and their arrangement. He made some progress in designating the period of mineralization, agreeing with Richthofen that the ores were deposited by hot waters ascending from greater depths.

King enjoyed maximum freedom in his relations with General Humphreys and the Corps of Engineers. The military left his science strictly alone, allowing him to handpick his staff and direct the parties in the field. He shifted the location of his office about as he pleased, from Washington, to New Haven, to New York. He sent Emmons to Europe for books, equipment, and advice. He was able to space his publishing activities to give himself time for mining and cattle ventures. General Humphreys intervened only when King wanted to suspend the mapping along the Pacific railroads. King had marked the watershed of the Green River in western Wyoming as the terminus of the study in historical geology, and when his parties reached this goal late in 1869, the field organization was disbanded and the staff returned to the East to prepare their findings for publication. The following year, however, Humphreys persuaded Congress to appropriate $100,000 for geographical surveys and military reconnaissances west of the Mississippi River, and he allotted one-half of the

9 *The American Journal of Science and Arts*, Third Series, I (1871), 219.
10 *The Comstock Lode: Its Formation and History* (New York, 1879), 29. Church worked for the U. S. Geographical Survey West of the One Hundredth Meridian.

sum to his civilian scientists. King planned to study volcanic cones from Arizona to Alaska, but Humphreys thought King had no legal basis for departing from the Pacific railroad axis and insisted the zonal mapping be carried farther east into Colorado and Wyoming to the longitude of Cheyenne.[11] For the short season in 1870 he permitted King to study volcanic cones on the west coast. While engaged in this study King and his assistants discovered glaciers, although European and American scientists had denied their existence in continental United States.[12]

One unforeseen result of Humphreys' decision was the involvement of the Fortieth Parallel Exploration in the dramatic diamond episode at the end of the exploration's last season in the field (1872). Clever thieves seeded on secret ground within Fortieth Parallel territory uncut diamonds worth thousands of dollars. One of the ablest mining engineers of the day was fooled into declaring that a genuine mine had been discovered. Bankers and Civil War generals planned to sell $10 million worth of stock, and the spurt of popular interest caused some people to anticipate a rush like the one in 1849. King and his men, however, discovered and exposed the fraud, inspiring some of the most positive declarations ever made in behalf of government science or scientists. "We have escaped, thanks to GOD and CLARENCE KING, a great financial calamity," wrote the editor of the San Francisco *Chronicle.* The San Francisco *Bulletin,* after saying that "Mr. King . . . has done the public a memorable service,"

[11] Clarence King to A. A. Humphreys, July 25, 1870, January 23, March 21, 1871, U. S. Geological Exploration of the Fortieth Parallel, Letters to the Chief of Engineers, 1867-1878; also, A. A. Humphreys to Clarence King, March 28, 1871, U. S. Geological Exploration of the Fortieth Parallel, Letters from Engineer Department, 1870-1881, U. S. National Archives.

[12] Clarence King, "On the Discovery of Actual Glaciers on the Mountains of the Pacific Slope," *American Journal of Science and Arts,* Third Series, I (1871), 158-60; see also Richard A. Bartlett, *Great Surveys of the American West* (Norman, 1962), 180-81.

acclaimed "the practical value, in the ordinary business of society, of scientific education and research. . . . These public surveys 'pay' in more senses than one, and even those who care nothing for wider and fuller knowledge for its own sake, must hereafter admit that Government expends no money more wisely and usefully."[13]

The diamond incident demonstrated that a privileged position within the corps was not enough to satisfy King. He renounced completely his connection with the corps by ignoring and deceiving General Humphreys.[14] He disguised his plans for locating the area which the swindlers had salted by telling his superior in October 1872 simply that he was leaving Fort Bridger in southwestern Wyoming for a short trip to the canyons of the Green River. Afterward, he reported doing a stratigraphical study at Lodore, although his search route never passed within miles of that canyon. He also pretended that geological reasoning led him to the diamond site. Ostensibly using his knowledge of the formation of diamonds, King decided that the strata most likely to produce the gems were certain Tertiary (Cenozoic) beds on the northern flank of the Uinta Mountains in extreme northwestern Colorado. He was describing accurately the location where the diamonds were found, but also where they could not have originated naturally, given the geological history of the region. As a matter of fact, geologist Emmons and topographer A. D. Wilson were the most instrumental persons in identifying the location, because they had been mapping in

[13] San Francisco *Chronicle*, November 28, 1872; San Francisco *Daily Evening Bulletin*, November 26, 1872. Clippings of these articles were enclosed in a letter from Clarence King to A. A. Humphreys, November 27, 1872, Chief of Engineers, Letters Received, 1867.

[14] Clarence King to A. A. Humphreys, November 27, 1872, *ibid.*; see the typed account in the S. F. Emmons Papers, Library of Congress. The location is designated by the names Ruby Gulch and Diamond Peak in Clarence King, *Geological and Topographical Atlas, Geological Exploration of the Fortieth Parallel*, Topographical Series, (Washington, 1876), Map II, Green River Basin, east half.

the area (where Colorado, Wyoming, and Utah come together) when several parties of the swindlers had visited there.[15]

When King informed the newspapers of the hoax before he reported it to General Humphreys, he was reprimanded, and military and bureaucratic control was reaffirmed. Whatever his private thoughts, Humphreys did not question the accuracy of the official report. He said that it was "eminently proper" for King to investigate the diamond mine since it lay within the limits of his exploration. Humphreys did object, however, to the manner of publication. He believed that the wisest course and "one more strictly in accordance with the regulations and custom of the service (which are founded upon long experience)" would have been for King to have mailed a brief official report at the nearest post office; to have requested authority to publish this report; and to have awaited in San Francisco the permission by telegraph, "which could have been so worded as to give no one any clue as to its meaning." This way of proceeding would have caused no material delay and would have been "in conformity to the established order by which the Engineer and War Departments are the first to be informed of the results of their operations."[16] Humphreys wrote privately, however, so King's exploit lost none of its public glamour.

Public reception of the geology proper was excellent. Members of the Fortieth Parallel Exploration had entered virgin territory with a recently developed science; they had brought back novel and interesting facts. *Descriptive Geology* (1877) by Emmons and Arnold Hague recorded surface features in the order of their appearance from Cheyenne to the eastern boundary of California. According to the English magazine

15 A. D. Wilson, "The Great California Diamond Mines: A True Story," *Overland Monthly*, XLIII (1904), 291-94; and a typed account in the Emmons Papers.

16 A. A. Humphreys to Clarence King, January 10, 1873, U. S. Geological Exploration of the Fortieth Parallel, Letters from Engineer Department, 1870-1881.

Nature, this book reinforced the reputation of King's party in terms of energy, zeal, great geological knowledge, and literary ability.[17] In *Systematic Geology* (1878) King was concerned with the same territory, organizing his historical study by eras. First, he sought to locate and describe the rocks which had been formed before the Cambrian period. In successive chapters he discussed the strata of the Paleozoic, Mesozoic, and Cenozoic eras, three of the grand divisions of geological time. He also proposed a sequence of geological events to explain western mountain building, which he associated closely with continental uplift.

Critics praised King's sound and progressive judgments. Relying on his knowledge of chemistry and mineralogy, King inferred one dry epoch and two humid epochs in the history of Lake Lahontan, a Pleistocene (Ice Age) body of water which once covered western Nevada. King's theories immediately were commended by geologists who specialized in Pleistocene era studies. Another geologist approved of King's theory that glacial erosion was an important force in mountain sculpture. King had drawn this conclusion from observation of the Uinta Mountains in northeastern Utah. Near the middle of the twentieth century a professional paper of the U. S. Geological Survey noted that King and Emmons had marked an angular unconformity east of Salt Lake City that geologists afterwards had overlooked, although this unconformity was evidence of important folding in the region of the central Wasatch Range sometime toward the middle of the Cretaceous period (Mesozoic era).[18]

By the time the exploration members published the geological volumes, King realized they would soon be obsolete. He was directing the "rapid exploration of a very great area";

[17] *Nature,* XVIII (1878), 538.

[18] Edmund M. Spieker, *Late Mesozoic and Early Cenozoic History of Central Utah,* Geological Survey Professional Paper No. 205-D (Washington, 1946), 150-51.

sooner or later detailed research would replace his hurried investigations.[19] Sequences of stratified rocks were a major interest of King and his company, but almost everywhere in Fortieth Parallel territory their successors have reconstituted the formations or series of them.[20] King and Emmons sometimes confused altered sedimentary rocks with those of igneous origin later introduced in the same locality, and they underestimated the complexity of mountain building near the transcontinental railroad.[21] Finally, King was partial to an old-fashioned interpretation of the nature of change on the earth's surface, continuing to think that change was sudden and violent even after most American geologists had rejected this view.[22]

Ultimately, the importance of the Exploration of the Fortieth Parallel lies elsewhere—in its mining program which King had executed promptly and skillfully. His conception of government science combined economic geology and technology. Its greatest significance was institutional, for it carried over into the founding and early years of the U. S. Geological Survey.

In 1867, the same year Clarence King joined the Corps of Army Engineers, F. V. Hayden became associated with the

[19] King, *Systematic Geology*, 4, xi.

[20] See, for example, J. M. Boutwell, *Geology and Ore Deposits of the Park City District, Utah*, Geological Survey Professional Paper No. 77 (Washington, 1912), 13, 42; James Gilluly, *Geology and Ore Deposits of the Stockton and Fairfield Quadrangles, Utah*, Geological Survey Professional Paper No. 173 (Washington, 1932), 4; Douglas M. Kinney, *Geology of the Uinta River-Brush Creek Area, Duchesne and Uinta Counties, Utah*, Geological Survey Bulletin No. 1007 (Washington, 1955), 18, 45.

[21] "The Little Cottonwood Granite Body of the Wasatch Mountains," *American Journal of Science*, Fourth Series, XVI (1903), 139-47; also Joseph Barrell, "A Century of Geology: The Growth of Knowledge of Earth Structure," *American Journal of Science*, Fourth Series, XLVI (1918), 146-47. Spieker, *Late Mesozoic and Early Cenozoic History of Central Utah*, 149.

[22] See below, pp. 84-89.

Department of the Interior. This department was interested in coal resources in the Nebraska Territory, and the Smithsonian Institution recommended Hayden as the man to direct a study of them.[23] After he had undertaken the government survey and concluded that prospects for coal in Nebraska were not good, Hayden in the following years pursued his interest in facts and theories of general geology and organized the U. S. Geological and Geographical Survey of the Territories. Because he developed so diversified a program and timed his projects skillfully to give them maximum popular appeal, he became the most powerful and most celebrated public scientist of the seventies. He had more funds to work with and directed the largest scientific staff in the territories. Westerners admired him as New Englanders had admired Louis Agassiz. For a time Hayden was the most famous American scientist to his English and European colleagues. He influenced greatly the early history of the U. S. Geological Survey, though his personal participation in the early Survey was negligible.

In pursuit of research Hayden traveled hundreds of miles every season between the Missouri River and Great Salt Lake. Unlike King, he did not intend connected history or two-dimensional mapping. His reports were primarily transcripts of daily notes on country through which he moved very rapidly. He marked the strata which dipped in one direction and those which folded into arches and troughs; he recognized mountains with granitic cores and those with a basaltic nucleus; he distinguished ridges of elevation from ridges of erosion and noted the sedimentary and metamorphic rocks.

[23] Hayden was born in western Massachusetts in 1829 and spent his early years in farming communities. He was educated first at Oberlin and then at Albany Medical College, where he received an M.D. in 1853. Instead of practicing medicine, he began to collect fossils and to observe geology in the upper Missouri River valley for scientists, local societies, or the War Department. He practiced as a doctor only during the Civil War—in the Union Army.

Also, he discovered some geological novelties—upsidedown beds and streams which cut their way through mountain ranges rather than following natural depressions. He reported correctly that the main ranges of the Rocky Mountains were gigantic upfolds and that the sea had not been in the Salt Lake Valley since at least middle Cenozoic time. Above all, Hayden was good at identifying formations and tracing them great distances. He gave special attention to fresh-water sedimentary rocks of the Cenozoic or modern era and to a Cretaceous series (Mesozoic time) of sandstone, shale, and limestone, still recognized by geologists, which he and F. B. Meek, a paleontologist, had previously put together from several places in the valley of the upper Missouri. He was particularly effective in following the upturned edges of these formations as they appeared along the eastern flank of the Rocky Mountains in the foothills of the Front Range. Sometimes Hayden was handicapped by his assumption that Rocky Mountain geology showed obvious and uniform features; he attempted, for example, to draw prematurely the line between the strata of the Mesozoic and Cenozoic eras. It has taken three generations of geological thought to reduce this complicated problem or solve it in the region of the Rocky Mountains.[24]

In 1871 Hayden greatly strengthened the public regard for his Survey of the Territories by engaging it in the movement to establish Yellowstone Park. As part of his exploration he led a summer expedition into the Yellowstone country, reports of whose geysers and hot springs had only recently been verified by curious citizens of the neighboring territory of Montana. After his return these same citizens, including W. H. Clagett, delegate to Congress, and N. P. Langford, territorial collector of internal revenue, proposed to withdraw the area

[24] Charles Schuchert and Carl O. Dunbar, *A Textbook of Geology: Part II: Historical Geology,* 3rd ed. (New York, 1933), 396-97; *Guide to the Geology of Colorado* (published by the Geological Society of America, the Rocky Mountain Association of Geologists, and the Colorado Scientific Society, Denver, 1960), 285-87.

from the public domain, and Hayden was called upon to locate the boundaries of the region.

Hayden and his knowledge were equally decisive in Congress. To the political canvassing during the winter of 1871-1872, when the three leaders collaborated to interview every member of Congress,[25] Hayden contributed photographs from his expedition taken by W. H. Jackson. Their scope, clarity, and detail must have conveyed the wonders of the Yellowstone as no words could possibly have done. In behalf of government ownership of the park, Hayden stressed the fact that the Yellowstone country could not support agriculture or mining. Every part of the Yellowstone area was unsuited for agriculture because of the altitude, and geological reasoning indicated the absence of valuable minerals. The sole attraction of the region was its hot springs and geysers, which represented a waning phase of extensive volcanic activity. Hayden eloquently predicted the consequences of legislative indifference. "Persons are now waiting for the spring to open," he wrote, "to enter in and take possession of these remarkable curiosities, to make merchandise of these beautiful specimens, to fence in these rare wonders, so as to charge visitors a fee." He further said that should the park bill fail to become law, vandals "will, in a single season, despoil, beyond recovery, these remarkable curiosities which have required all the cunning skill of nature thousands of years to prepare."[26] His arguments were incorporated verbatim into the favorable report by the House of Representatives committee on the public lands. Senators cited the same arguments, and both houses found it effective to name Hayden as a sponsor of the bill. He had already won congressional approval for Yellowstone by securing an appropriation to lead an expedition

[25] *Diary of the Washburn Expedition to Yellowstone and Firehole Rivers in the Year 1870,* ed. N. P. Langford (Saint Paul, 1905), Introduction, xxii.
[26] F. V. Hayden, *Preliminary Report of the U. S. Geological Survey of Montana* (Washington, 1872), 164.

there, and he also was the scientist who could speak with authority on that country. On March 1, 1872, President Grant signed the bill, and 3,000 square miles near the headwaters of the Yellowstone River were set aside as a public park for the benefit and enjoyment of the American people.

The rewards for Hayden were substantial. His appropriation was doubled in 1872 to $75,000, where it remained for the rest of the decade. American scientists, as well as the general public, endorsed the Yellowstone withdrawal. It won Hayden a place in American history. And he had created a new and substantial responsibility for government geologists. In 1883 a division of Yellowstone Park was organized within the U. S. Geological Survey to maintain and improve the area.

In 1873 the U. S. Geological and Geographical Survey of the Territories entered Colorado, where Hayden saw an inviting prospect. The mining industry was active in the area, the railroads were extending their lines, and statehood was imminent. A topographical and geological atlas for the region west of the longitude of Denver would be valuable. To strengthen his staff, Hayden hired J. T. Gardiner, King's chief topographer, and assigned him to mapping physical features. The annual reports, published quickly after the summer's labor, were to produce a steady flow of geological information. Probably the best scientific writing was by A. R. Marvine, who devoted the summer of 1873 to the Front Range and Middle Park, a mountain and basin area beyond Denver; his account of the pre-Cambrian core of the Front Range was characterized, 60 years later, as one of the best ever written.[27] Near Colorado Springs, Hayden described and sketched erosion-formed columns of sandstone, protected by a hard capping of oxide of iron. In the Eagle River region of central Colorado he dis-

[27] T. S. Lovering, *Geology and Ore Deposits of the Montezuma Quadrangle, Colorado*, Geological Survey Professional Paper No. 178 (Washington, 1934), 5.

covered humps of bedrock smoothed and polished by ice abra-
sion so that seen from above they resembled a flock of huge
sheep.[28] Another member of Hayden's survey, A. C. Peale, reported correctly the broader lines of geological structure in
western Colorado. He also drew many vertical sections to reveal
the successive strata, comparing these sections with their
counterparts in other regions, but failed to give them satisfactory boundaries.[29] Perhaps the annual reports of geologist
F. M. Endlich imitated too literally Hayden's arrangement of
the strata. Hesitating to subdivide or amend established descriptions of formations, he made no important contribution
to stratigraphy. Yet Endlich visited the Summitville mining
district in the San Juan Mountains of southwestern Colorado
and from one day's observations, based upon only four mine
openings, gave a "remarkably perceptive" account of the
geology there.[30] The Survey of the Territories benefited from
the artistic and scientific craftsmanship of W. H. Holmes,
whose sketches were as good as photographs in presenting
knowledge visually.

The publication of Hayden's atlas in 1878 was hailed as
an international event from Denver to Moscow. The state
legislature of Colorado passed a resolution thanking him and
saying that his maps were "invaluable alike" for science, mining, and agriculture.[31] James D. Dana praised the "beautiful
series of plates, the best the country has produced in map-

[28] *Annual Report of the U.S. Geological and Geographical Survey of the Territories* (Washington, 1876), 36-37; F. V. Hayden, *Annual Report of the U.S. Geological and Geographical Survey of the Territories, Embracing Colorado* (Washington, 1874), 72-73.

[29] Quentin D. Singewald, *Stratigraphy, Structure, and Mineralization in the Beaver-Tarryall Area, Park County, Colorado,* Geological Survey Bulletin No. 928-A (Washington, 1942), 5-6.

[30] Thomas A. Stevens and James C. Ratté, *Geology and Ore Deposits of the Summitville District, San Juan Mountains, Colorado,* Geological Survey Professional Paper No. 343 (Washington, 1960), 7.

[31] *Extracts from Letters and Notices of Eminent Scientific Men and Journals in Europe and America, Commendatory of the United States Geological and Geographical Survey of the Territories* (1879), 4.

photo-lithography."[32] Another geologist, Jules Marcou, praised the quality of the science and the panoramic views. The volume was applauded by many other prominent American and European scientists.

The youngest state in the Union now had the best topographical and geological maps. They were not serviceable for intensive research, but they gave a good representation of general features, and prospectors used them for decades. The only serious criticism was the omission of an explanatory text.

Hayden gave his Survey of the Territories its final dimension when he began publishing research in paleontology and natural history. All the post-Civil War surveys recognized these disciplines, but only Hayden had the resources and the determination to make them primary topics in his studies. His most famous paleontologist was E. D. Cope, who established numerous genera in mammals, reptiles, and fish. Leo Lesquereux, Hayden's other distinguished paleontologist, investigated Cretaceous and Cenozoic flora beyond the Mississippi.[33] Not only did Hayden provide encouragement for natural history and paleontology, but he also invented new methods of communication—his progress reports and bulletins, which were much more quickly produced than the long, scholarly monographs that had been the characteristic product of government science. Hayden opened these new publication channels to American scientists, who used the bulletins to publish heavily in botany and zoology. Any article proved acceptable so long as the locus of study was North America. The future Geological Survey would adopt the bulletin for speedier publication, and paleontology would have a central position among the sciences.

[32] J. D. Dana to F. V. Hayden, July 18, 1878, U. S. Geological and Geographical Survey of the Territories, Letters Received, 1877, U. S. National Archives.

[33] H. F. Osborn, *Cope: Master Naturalist* (New York, 1931), 498, 505-506. Leo Lesquereux, *The Cretaceous Flora* (Washington, 1874); *The Tertiary Flora* (Washington, 1878); *The Cretaceous and Tertiary Flora* (Washington, 1883); *The Flora of the Dakota Group* (Washington, 1891).

In the 1870's, following King and Hayden, John Wesley Powell established his survey in the Colorado River region of western America. This survey laid the foundations for a new division of earth science, which was known as the American school of geology. Also, Powell acquired an interest in land reclamation, which he expanded into a national program when he succeeded King as director of the Survey. As director both his successes and his failures would be extraordinary.

A one-armed veteran of Shiloh, Powell wanted first to be a famous explorer.[34] He looked at the authoritative map of the territories by the Corps of Engineers and saw a large gap along the Colorado River in Utah and Arizona. This unexplored region was, he said, "a reproach to the boasted enterprise of our people."[35] As a naturalist he had a leaning toward geology, and he believed that he could assemble "the best geological section on the continent," if he rowed down the Colorado River into the Grand Canyon.[36] In the Senate, where he went in 1868 for free army rations for his Illinois-sponsored venture, it was said that the army engineers had already been to the canyon. But Senator Conness of California knew better. Easterners, he replied, did not appreciate the size of the West and how much of it still remained unexplored.[37] In dramatizing his expedition and appealing to the curiosity of the American people, Powell exaggerated the mystery of the river and its environs, which he called the "Great Unknown." When explaining to the readers of the Chicago *Tribune* the purpose of his expedition just before he departed in the spring of 1869, he wrote that "after three

[34] He was born in upstate New York in 1834, but most of his early life was spent in the Middle West. In Illinois during the 1850's he moved slowly from farming to nature study. Although he attended several colleges, he never took a degree. After the Civil War he was on the faculties of Illinois Wesleyan and Illinois Normal Universities.

[35] L. F. Ward, "Sketch of J. W. Powell," *Glimpses of the Cosmos,* II (New York, 1913), 429.

[36] J. W. Powell to U. S. Grant, April 2, 1868, U. S., *Congressional Globe,* 40th Cong., 2nd Sess., 2407.

[37] U. S., *Congressional Globe,* 40th Cong., 2nd Sess., May 25, 1868, p. 2564.

years' study" he thought it "doubtful" whether the Colorado
canyons had "ever been seen by man." This statement
prompted a protesting letter from J. S. Newberry, geologist
and paleontologist of Columbia College, who had been on
two expeditions sponsored by the War Department to the
canyon country. Also citing the Spanish explorer Escalante,
Newberry concluded that if Powell had really meant what he
said, then "he is not so well informed in regard to his field
of operations as the leader of his expedition should be."[38]
Glory came, nevertheless, after Powell explored the river for
900 miles, and in 1870 he entered the federal service.

Powell and his survey effected a shift of emphasis within
geology. The members of the King and Hayden organizations
had been in the mainstream of nineteenth-century geological
effort. They were primarily stratigraphers, attempting to put
formations in their proper order, to correlate local sequences
with formations elsewhere, and in general to use the strata
for understanding the history of the earth. Powell himself
went west to make a canyon section, and he published an
excellent description of formations near the Uinta Mountains,
an east-west range in northeastern Utah, extending parallel
to the Wyoming border into northwestern Colorado.[39] For
the most part, however, this third group of federal scientists
did not construct geological columns.' Instead, they studied
topographic features, hoping to explain landscape forms and
patterns through discovery of the natural processes which
caused them. They were students of earth sculpture, or what
is now called geomorphology (literally, knowledge of the shape
of the ground). Previous study of glacial effects on land forms
in the East had aroused their curiosity about the origin of
surface features. So when these scientists saw the abrupt, bare,
and angular landscape of the plateau and canyon country,
contrasting so obviously with the rounded and covered fea-

38 Chicago *Tribune*, May 24, June 4, 1869.
39 Kinney, *Geology of the Uinta River-Brush Creek Area*, 18.

tures of eastern topography, they determined to investigate the causes of the different form.

Powell's interest was the process of erosion, which geologists already knew had carved the canyons. He concluded that erosion was a powerful force, even against mountains. Weather and stream could wear down any land mass, however extensive, and leave only a lowland sloping gently to the margin of its adjacent sea. "Mountains," he wrote vividly, "cannot remain long as mountains; they are ephemeral topographical forms. Geologically speaking, all existing mountains are recent; the ancient mountains are gone."[40] Using the physiographic facts, Powell began to shape the vocabulary of geomorphology. "Base level of erosion" was a term he invented, designating a plane surface below which dry land could not be worn away, because there was no slope to energize streams. Sea level was an example, and so (temporarily) were the beds of large streams. Using the concept of the base level of erosion, Powell saw the continuity of valley erosion and hill degradation. This discovery, in effect, was the beginning of geomorphology as a branch of geological knowledge. "The first work of rains and rivers is to cut channels, and divide the country into hills, and perhaps, mountains, by many meandering grooves or water-courses, and when these have reached their local base levels, under the existing conditions, the hills are washed down, but not carried entirely away."[41]

Powell defined three kinds of valleys or drainage systems— consequent, antecedent, and superimposed or superposed.[42] In a consequent valley the drainage depended upon the previously established landscape. The direction of streamflow was said to be consequent to the initial slope. Powell cited as

[40] Report on the Geology of the Eastern Portion of the Uinta Mountains (Washington, 1876), 196.
[41] Exploration of the Colorado River of the West and its Tributaries (Washington, 1875), 204.
[42] Ibid., 163-66.

an antecedent gorge or portion of a valley the Lodore Canyon, the route for the Green River through the Uinta Mountains, and an adventurous stage of his voyage down the Colorado. By principles of physical geography he knew it would have been easier for the river to go around the mountains. Its passage through the mountains meant that the river was there first; its course was antecedent to the mountains. Flowing before the Uinta Range was uplifted, the Green River maintained its right-of-way by cutting a canyon through the rising mountains. Today, geologists do not agree with Powell, believing instead that the Lodore Canyon belongs to the third kind of valley outlined by him. The drainage of the Green River was superposed or let down upon a preexisting mountain structure. The river once flowed south over a mantle of sediments, which covered the eastern portion of the Uinta Range. Cutting its valley downward through this cover mass, the river encountered the buried mountains, and, by attacking them without diverting its course, excavated the canyon.[43] This criticism has not discredited Powell's research in the Uinta Mountains. Experts still regard his efforts as masterly, better than anything by Clarence King, who worked nearby in the same mountains.[44]

Prior to the 1875 field season Powell hired Grove Karl Gilbert, whose research with the government was to make him one of the immortals of modern geology. Land forms had been Gilbert's interest when he served with the Corps of Engineers. He studied the forces which counteracted the power of erosion and built up or elevated the earth's surface. In Powell's survey Gilbert identified a new kind of uplift in the Henry Mountains (a range in southeastern Utah, discovered by Powell). Geologists knew that molten rock material

[43] William D. Thornbury, *Principles of Geomorphology* (New York, 1954), 113-19.

[44] Julian D. Sears, staff geologist, to Wilmot H. Bradley, chief geologist, February 15, 1955, U. S. Geological Survey, Memorandum, 1955.

could rise to the earth's surface and form hills or mountains. The magma, as the molten material is called, starting from an unknown depth, passed through the rock systems to open space where it piled up. Gilbert concluded that the magma at the location of the Henry Mountains had not followed the typical pattern. Instead of rising through the formations, it intruded among them and made chambers by pushing upward the overlying strata. It solidified in these chambers, forming bodies of trap called laccolites, or later laccoliths.[45] The up-arching of the strata produced domelike hills on the surface, which then were subject to erosion, sometimes enough to expose the underlying laccoliths. Since Gilbert's time, geologists have studied igneous mountains for laccolithic structure, often finding such a phenomenon. Gilbert's opinions have been modified, however, for geologists now believe that these igneous bodies do not come as large as he thought. In the Henry Mountains, for example, the main peaks are no longer classified as laccoliths, but are held to be the products of igneous bodies without any known floor, called stocks. There are laccoliths in the Henry Mountains, but they seem to be smaller masses, formed as tongue-like extensions from stocks.[46]

In the same report on the Henry Mountains, Gilbert devoted 50 pages to the principles of earth sculpture by rain and water, "as derived or enforced by the study of the Colorado Plateau."[47] Three generations of geologists, physiographers, and geographers have praised this chapter, which is regarded as a classic of geomorphology. A few illustrations will show the scope and power of Gilbert's thinking. He conceived the evolution of topographic forms as conditioned by

[45] G. K. Gilbert, *Report on the Geology of the Henry Mountains* (Washington, 1877), 18-21.

[46] Charles B. Hunt, assisted by Paul Averitt and Ralph H. Miller, *Geology and Geography of the Henry Mountains Region, Utah,* Geological Survey Professional Paper No. 228 (Washington, 1953), 1, 90.

[47] Gilbert, *Geology of the Henry Mountains,* 99.

three fundamental laws. The law of structure stated a relationship of hard and soft rocks. Because erosion was more rapid where the resistance was lower, the soft rocks were worn away and the hard ones left prominent. The law of declivities explained the profiles or slopes of drainage lines. The nearer the slope to the divide between watersheds, the steeper that slope will be; the more distant the slope from the divide, the gentler it will be. Because climate was the factor that determined the relative importance of the laws of structure and declivities, Gilbert ranked it as the third condition of sculpture. Modern textbooks still include his generalization about unequal slopes.[48] Given homogeneous material and equal quantities of water, the rate of erosion on two slopes will vary with their steepness. When these two slopes are on opposite sides of a divide, the steeper, because it wears away more rapidly, will carry the divide toward the side of the gentler. The divide ceases to move in this way only when its profile has become symmetrical. Contemporary geologists also use his interpretation of formation of terraces along the course of a river. Gilbert found the obvious explanation—that these terraces were formed by a deposition from the river—to be wrong. He saw that they were carved mainly by the river from remnants of a former valley floor.[49]

The paradox of the Powell survey was that it produced the highest quality science, yet it was the weakest politically and financially. In the beginning the research had broad appeal and, therefore, political strength, because it involved adventure as well as pursuit of knowledge. But after the initial excitement had passed, Powell stressed the development of scientific principles and understanding in ethnology as well as in geology and neglected popular reaction or practical

---

[48] See the textbook, Thornbury, *Principles of Geomorphology*, 151.
[49] C. A. Cotton, *Geomorphology: An Introduction to the Study of Land Forms*, 5th ed. (New York, 1949), 244.

service. Unlike Hayden, he did not strain continually for the renewal of his fame as a scientist. Unlike King, he had no alliance with an economic interest. He carried his indifference to public appeal so far that congressmen had to pressure him to publish annual reports. Powell would have preferred to demonstrate the value of his survey through the finished monograph studies. The legislators associated him with pure science, placing his survey for several years under the aegis of the organization in Washington that epitomized original research, the Smithsonian Institution. The grave consequence of Powell's insensitivity to public response was insecurity. Every year his appropriation read as if it were to be the last, and he always seemed short of money. Acting upon a suggestion of Joseph Henry, secretary of the Smithsonian, Powell began a study of irrigation, which was practical enough, though on the periphery of geological studies. In 1878 he published his famous *Report on the Lands of the Arid Region of the United States, with a more Detailed Account of the Lands of Utah.*

Powell's message in *Lands of the Arid Region* was that only a small portion of the large expanse of territory in western America was suitable for agriculture. His boundary of the arid region began near the one hundredth meridian at the isohyetal line of 20 inches of annual precipitation. Almost all the land beyond this line, two-fifths of continental United States, lacked the minimum 20 inches of precipitation which allowed continuous cultivation without irrigation. And there was only sufficient stream water to irrigate three percent of this huge area. Today, arid lands are not measured by average annual rainfall or by any other single factor. Moisture in the soil depends on a variety of factors—first on total rainfall, as modified by slope, plant cover, and soil permeability, and secondly on evaporation, which expresses the climatic interchange among temperature, humidity, cloudiness, and wind. Detailed investigations of all the features of each drainage basin

are desirable, scientists say, before ground can be designated for
proper use.[50] These refinements do not undermine the merit
of Powell's report. He rejected the myth of increasing rainfall in newly occupied areas. He used rainfall statistics, compiled at the Smithsonian Institution, to give his thinking a
quantitative basis. He sent Gilbert into the communities of
Utah during the summer of 1877 to observe irrigation practice, and this extraordinary assistant drafted an equation for
the duty of water, or how much land a given water supply
would serve.[51] Powell carried Gilbert's figures on irrigation
in the Mormon community to the American people, along
with a topographical map overlaid in color, showing the irrigable, timber, and pasturage lands of Utah. The study of
arid lands was turning toward scientific channels.[52]

Powell hoped that one contribution of his report would
be revision of the government's land laws to adapt them to
the arid region.[53] The rigid, rectangular lines of surveying
should be replaced by flexibly-shaped parcels so that every
owner could reach water. The size of the allotments should
be reduced since 80 acres were enough for an irrigation farm.
The homesteader must change his individualistic ways; he
was no longer free to settle by a stream and seize all the water
he pleased. Persons must form irrigation districts and admin-
ister collectively the precious resource. Groups of cattlemen,

[50] *The Future of the Arid Lands,* ed. Gilbert F. White (Washington,
1956), 28-30, 77, 158, 235.

[51] G. K. Gilbert, "Irrigable Lands of the Salt Lake Drainage System,"
in J. W. Powell, *Lands of the Arid Region,* 112-16.

Gilbert was welcome because he carried a letter from Brigham Young.
The aged leader remembered Powell: "He has had a great desire to see
you," Gilbert wrote, "ever since he learned that a piece of bacon which
Fremont threw away and which the wolves failed to find has been
recently discovered in a petrified condition." G. K. Gilbert to J. W. Powell,
June 28, 1877, U. S. Geographical and Geological Survey of the Rocky
Mountain Region (Powell's final name in 1876 for his survey), Letters
Received, 1877, U. S. National Archives.

[52] On the land classification, see J. W. Powell, *Lands of the Arid Region,*
6-9, 14-18, 19-21.

[53] *Ibid.,* 28-29, 39.

each with 2,500 acres and access to water, might also organize districts.

Lands of the Arid Region circulated widely, opening the future to Powell. When the report appeared as a congressional publication in September 1878, the western newspapers paid little attention, but the first edition of 1,900 copies was soon exhausted. Early in the following year Congress declared a second edition of 5,000 copies. Powell now was an authority on the public domain and one of the nation's experts on its irrigable lands. He later testified that thousands of people settled in Utah on land which he had marked as irrigable on his map of 1878. From his new vantage point he would twice try to advance his ideas in American politics, first during the movement toward a united survey in 1879 and again 10 years later when he was director of the Geological Survey.

Chapter Two

THE FOUNDING OF THE
U. S. GEOLOGICAL SURVEY IN 1879

The movement for a united geological survey was the reaction
to an intersurvey rivalry which brought disorder to government science, reduced public confidence in it, and even threatened its extinction. Hayden and Powell clashed with the
Corps of Engineers, who, after King had left the field, established their own survey under the command of Lieutenant
George M. Wheeler. The engineers wished to regain the
prominence in science in the western territories which they
once enjoyed. Powell would maintain the independence which
he and the other geologists recently had acquired. Hayden,
more than any other military or civilian person, wanted to
dominate western science, and his attitude even led to quar-
reling with Powell. The Pacific railroad enhanced this rivalry
by drawing into close and bruising contact scientists who initially were physically distant from one another. Using the
railroad, the various survey leaders could move swiftly into
new places. To counter the disorder and to appease the rising
congressional discontent a group within the National Academy of Sciences urged consolidation of the surveys under civilian control. In the academy plan the existing western
surveys were to be abolished, and a United States Geological
Survey was to take their place. The academy scientists prepared a program for economy in government science, which
did not include natural history, downgraded paleontology,
and moved ethnology into the Smithsonian Institution. Congress welcomed the proposed changes and broadened the economy move by nullifying land classification and curbing

topographical mapping. The legislators also specified that economic geology should be the core science of the new civilian bureau. The final testing for government science and its scientists came with the struggle for the directorship between Hayden and King, which President Hayes decided in favor of King.

An important factor in the rivalry that preceded the founding of the U. S. Geological Survey was the resumption by the army engineers of topographical mapping in the western territories. In 1873 General Humphreys promised an atlas of 95 sheets to be prepared by the United States Geographical Survey West of the One Hundredth Meridian under the direction of Lieutenant G. M. Wheeler, a recent graduate of West Point. During the 1870's, 50 sheets were published by the Wheeler survey, mostly from Colorado and the Southwest.[1]

Topography was a science which the army engineers had developed and could justify with confidence as government business. "Topography," Wheeler said, "has grown up a permanent unvarying essential of the military profession" and *"in all large and well-organized Governments it . . . is now found under military administration, and everywhere, without exception, military officers, alone, are eligible to the direction and control of such works."*[2] The U. S. Army, now campaigning against the Indians, required good maps, and the Geographical Survey West of the One Hundredth Meridian would provide them. Wheeler's maps were better than those of any other army engineer, as they were continuous over wide areas

[1] G. M. Wheeler to A. A. Humphreys, February 3, 1873, Chief of Engineers, Letters Received, 1873; G. M. Wheeler, *Report on Geographical Surveys West of the One Hundredth Meridian, I, Geographical Report* (Washington, 1889), 46, 138-40, 146.

[2] *Report upon the Third International Geographical Congress and Exhibition at Venice, Italy, 1881, Accompanied by Data Concerning the Principal Government Land and Marine Surveys of the World,* U. S., House Ex. Doc. No. 270, 48th Cong., 2nd Sess., 85, 157.

rather than along discrete lines of marches. Before plans had matured, he claimed only an accuracy in "between the Reconnaissances known as the Pacific Rail Road surveys and a more careful Geodetic and Geological Survey such as is now being conducted along the 40th Parallel."[3] Within the limits of his professional standards, Wheeler tended to give more detail, a greater number of fixed positions, and a variety of finer scales.

Even though geology had lost the primacy given to it in civilian surveys, significant research still was being done; above all by Gilbert, who, before joining Powell, had served three seasons with the Survey West of the One Hundredth Meridian. Gilbert advanced a new theory of mountain building, which, although incomplete, was adopted among geologists. The earliest modern ideas derived from the Alps, where the conspicuous feature was plication or folding. When geology was colonized in America, research in the Appalachians reaffirmed these observations; like the Alps, the Appalachians were plicated ridges resulting from horizontal pressures. In the Far West geologists of the Fortieth Parallel Exploration offered this customary explanation, but Gilbert found land masses in their territory—the Great Basin—which had arisen without lateral compression. This Basin Range structure developed out of country broken into large blocks by faulting. When these blocks had tilted so much that the strata dipped at high angles, the uplifted edges formed mountain ridges. This involved primarily the vertical movement of adjacent blocks of the earth's crust.[4]

To execute the corps plan of 1873, Wheeler came from the Southwest to the territory of Colorado. Simultaneously, Hayden began his famous atlas. The clashes between the two sur-

[3] G. M. Wheeler to A. A. Humphreys, February 21, 1871, Chief of Engineers, Letters Received, 1871.

[4] G. K. Gilbert, *On the Geology of Portions of Our Western Territory Visited in the Years 1871, 1872 and 1873* (Washington, 1876), 41-42, 61-62.

veys, both in the field and in Washington, were spectacular. Hayden called Wheeler provocative, threatened to "crush" him, and said he would forever exclude army officers from western explorations or surveys. He boasted that with his military antagonist out of the way he could easily absorb all territorial science. Wheeler and the engineers reacted to this by accusing Hayden of telling lies. First, Hayden had said he would stay in Wyoming for the summer; nevertheless he went to Colorado. Next, he announced he would do no work in the main range of the Rocky Mountains, yet army parties kept meeting Hayden's scientists west and southwest of Denver.[5] The confrontation and flurry of statements brought congressional intervention. In the spring of 1874 the House committee on public lands held a week-long series of hearings. The Departments of War and the Interior were represented by their secretaries, W. W. Belknap and Columbus Delano, respectively. President Grant wrote on behalf of the military, and J. W. Powell supported Hayden.

The hearings demonstrated that Hayden was speaking not only for himself, but also for a rising, aggressive class of American scientists. They were the new intellectuals, unhappy at the prospect of serving under army officers who did not have their scientific training and often showed lack of "sympathy for scientific pursuits." They complained also that discoveries by army surveys were classified "for use of the Department" only.[6] These scientists now rallied to Hayden. Faculty petitions supporting him and bearing some 50 signatures came from Harvard, Yale, and the Massachusetts Institute of Technology. Three renowned geologists, J. D. Dana, W. B. Rogers, and J. D. Whitney, sent personal letters. The engineers seemed

[5] See the affidavits in "Surveys West of the Mississippi," 63, 71-73. J. S. Newberry to O. C. Marsh, March 24, 1874, O. C. Marsh Papers, Yale University. W. L. Marshall to G. M. Wheeler, March 1, 1874, Chief of Engineers, Letters Received, 1874.

[6] W. H. Brewer to J. R. Hawley, May 13, 1874, "Surveys West of the Mississippi," 60.

stupified; they could not believe that the old order of scientific research in the western territories had gone. General Humphreys denied alienation between civilian and military scientists. Wheeler criticized civilian manners and ethics, calling Gardiner, for example, "traitorous" because he had left the Exploration of the Fortieth Parallel to join Hayden in Colorado.[7]

The question before the House committee on public lands centered upon topographical mapping. According to the engineers, this mapping was what a public survey should do. Lieutenant Wheeler aimed "in the most perfect manner" to bring all science "to the cause of geography."[8] General Humphreys said mapping by army officers in the trans-Mississippi West went back to Lewis and Clark. In Europe the army's operations and surveys were considered "models of their kind."[9] The general attributed this success to the superior education of engineer officers, who possessed "the highest acquirements" in "geography (and astronomy), geodesy, topography, hydrography and meteorology."[10] The remote location of the western surveys was also advanced in support of military control. A man who led an expedition into the interior must know how to command. President Grant said that all such expeditions required a military escort; General Humphreys knew of very few which were unaccompanied by troops. On several occasions Hayden and King had needed soldiers, and all the postwar surveys had called upon the War Department for arms, supplies, and transportation.[11]

The civilians also believed that a scientific survey should include topographical mapping, but they favored a contour

7 "Surveys West of the Mississippi," 67, 73-77.

8 *Ibid.*, 78.

9 A. A. Humphreys to W. W. Belknap, April 23, 1874, *ibid.*, 4.

10 A. A. Humphreys to C. L. Merriam, February 5, 1873, Chief of Engineers, Letters Sent, 1873.

11 U. S. Grant to U. S. House of Representatives, April 30, 1874, and W. W. Belknap to U. S. Grant, April 27, 1874, "Surveys West of the Mississippi," 2.

map which would accept overlays of geological color, and Wheeler's maps lacked the necessary continuity and detail. Gardiner found areas in the Southwest as large as Rhode Island or Connecticut which the engineers had marched around. He contrasted a sheet by Wheeler from the Southwest, which gave 40 elevations, with his own of an equal area in Colorado, which listed several thousand altitudes. Powell, very much the college professor, used blackboard and diagrams to analyze a Wheeler map from Utah. He pointed out half a dozen places where physical features on the War Department map could not stand intelligent discussion or delineation of geological structure. The civilian scientists in the Department of the Interior placed their *dual* mapping in a nonmilitary context. Their surveys would ascertain geological structure and classify the lands of the public domain for economic use. Such surveys would help the government to identify and dispose of its timber, coal, and irrigable properties.

Nor were military escorts necessary, Powell argued. He spoke half a dozen native dialects and bragged that he could even go among the Apaches without fear. He said armed men were the poorest introduction to the ethnological studies, which were part of his survey.

The House committee did not try to resolve the problem of competing surveys; rather, it sought to mediate between the civilian and military commands. Each survey group admitted that the others had worthwhile scientific duties in the public domain. Humphreys agreed that geology connected with the land surveys belonged properly to the Department of the Interior. Powell, Gardiner, and the Secretary of the Interior all conceded that the War Department should do mapping for military defense. The politicians found evidence about the controversy in Colorado to be "directly contradictory and of equal weight on both sides." Wheeler and Hayden were reprimanded for "ill-judged and hasty expressions . . . which good taste would have withheld." The present expectation of the committee was that "a generous rivalry" stimulating the two departments and preventing disorder would develop. The secretaries would never "be so wanting in attention to the public interests as to send out surveying parties that will be overlapping each other and duplicating their labors at a loss to the people." In the long run the nonmilitary scientific surveys would prevail. For as settlement progressed, knowledge of natural resources would be more in demand than military geography. In impressive numbers civilian scientists wanted to go west; already they were a large component in Wheeler's topographic parties (the Corps of Engineers could never spare more than half a dozen of its 100 officers for territorial duties). Therefore, the committee concluded, if ever consolidation should occur with the purpose of constructing "a grand geographical map" of the territories, the Department of the Interior should take charge.[12]

That part of the House appeal to the common interest of the several surveys proved unrealistic and ineffective. The conclusion that the Secretary of the Interior drew from the investigation was that his department should make plans for a geographical atlas, and he instructed Hayden and Powell where to map. Now two departmental atlases were authorized, with no understanding about areas of operation. Before 1874 Powell and Wheeler had mapped an identical 26,000 square miles in the Southwest; by 1878 the extent of this repetition had doubled, mostly in Colorado. One scientist compiled a list of mountain peaks in Colorado, each with two names, one from Wheeler and one from Hayden.

The civilian scientists quarreled among themselves where the Secretary of the Interior had not laid down clear lines of demarcation. In 1877 Hayden approved W. H. Jackson's plans for photographing pueblo settlements in northeastern Arizona, and Hayden considered moving his survey there to investigate

12 *Ibid.*, 16-18.

Indian life. This southward move from Colorado provoked
Powell, the leader in western ethnological studies, and he appealed to Secretary of the Interior Carl Schurz, complaining
of Hayden's encroachment on his ground. Hayden promised
to send no one to Arizona. Powell then proposed that each
terminate operations in one of the other's specialities; thus,
he would drop studies in natural history, and Hayden would
discontinue ethnology. This division of labor took effect immediately and was recognized as departmental policy in
November.

Powell, however, still seemed reluctant to enter wholeheart-
edly into the harsh, competitive politics of science. He apolo-
gized to Newberry of Columbia College for behaving like a
boy during the encounter with Hayden in the secretary's office.
His indignation, he explained, was only a move against "rivalry and indecent haste to publish . . . a contest in which
I have never entered nor shall I in the future."[13] There is no
evidence that he ever wanted or tried to capture the other
surveys.

The climax of the struggle came in Congress where Hayden
was strong. During the 1870's he established understandings
with W. S. Holman, representative from Indiana, and A. A.
Sargent, representative and senator from California. Two
others reputed to be his good friends were Senator John A.
Logan of Illinois and H. L. Dawes of Massachusetts, who
was in the Senate after 1875. Logan, Dawes, and Holman
each had sons in Hayden's field parties for one or more years.
If Hayden had been striving simply to protect his own appropriation, no one could have objected, but simultaneously he
was maneuvering against Wheeler and Powell. In 1876 Wheeler's appropriation was eliminated in the House—probably at
the instigation of Hayden—and restored in the Senate. Early
the next year Newberry learned that Holman of the committee

13 J. W. Powell to J. S. Newberry, June 7, 1877, Rocky Mountain Region
Survey, Letters Sent, 1877.

on appropriations was prepared to oppose all surveys except Hayden's, but the other members of the committee would defend Powell, Newberry said. Powell feared it would be a "tight squeeze."[14] When this attack failed, Hayden tried again in 1878, introducing through Representative J. D. C. Atkins of Tennessee resolutions of inquiry about the various surveys, which might very well start a movement for consolidation in his favor.

Hayden's aggressiveness and the congressional response were indicative of the change in the position of government science that gradually had taken place during the 1870's. For a time after Appomattox, Congress had welcomed the new scientific surveys. Then a reaction developed, and influential members of Congress began investigations or demanded economy. The desire to arrest this political deterioration and to stabilize government science led to the movement for a united geological survey.

Clarence King, Representative Abram Stevens Hewitt of New York City, and Representative Atkins of Tennessee were responsible for asking the National Academy of Sciences to evaluate the scientific surveys. King first proposed to involve the academy, talking on March 15, 1878, with J. J. Stevenson, a geologist who had recently made an agreement with Wheeler for a field program in southern California and northern New Mexico under terms that gave him freedom from military regulations and authorized him to select all assistants. The news of Atkins' resolutions distressed Stevenson, for he feared the

14 J. W. Powell to J. S. Newberry, January 25, 1877, *ibid.*, Letters Sent, 1877.

J. S. Newberry to J. W. Powell, January 22, 23, 1877, *ibid.*, Letters Received, 1877; J. J. Stevenson to O. C. Marsh, March 15, 1878, Marsh Papers; Washington Townsend to F. V. Hayden, June 26, 1876, U. S. Geological and Geographical Survey of the Territories, Letters Received, 1876; U. S., *Congressional Record,* 44th Cong., 1st Sess., June 24, 1876, pp. 4097, 4098, 4112.

beginning of a campaign by Hayden to eliminate Wheeler. Replying, King thought "some senator" should "move that the whole matter of these surveys be referred to the National Academy to report on the competence of the persons in charge of the several surveys."[15]

Within the House committee on appropriations Hewitt and Atkins, repudiating the investigation of personalities, inserted a clause in the Sundry Civil Appropriation Bill calling upon the National Academy of Sciences to propose "a plan for surveying and mapping the Territories of the United States," which would take "into consideration the methods and expenses of conducting all surveys of a scientific character under the War or Interior Department, and the surveys of the Land Office."[16]

With this resolution Hewitt assumed a leading part in the consolidation movement. He was a partner in the firm of Cooper, Hewitt, and Company, pioneers in the mass production of iron and steel. While in Congress he kept up with technology, and he sat as a director for railroad and mining companies. On legislation to exploit mineral resources he was the nearest thing to a practical expert that the House had. Paradoxically, this forward-looking man, even as he helped prepare the resolution, was thinking in traditional terms. Scientific surveys, he believed, belonged under military control.[17]

The request to the National Academy of Sciences, which became law on June 20, 1878, placed O. C. Marsh, the paleontologist of Yale College, in the center of the struggle over the western surveys. Marsh was vice-president of the academy and its leader since the death of President Joseph Henry in May. He soon learned that at least two important members, J. E. Hilgard, home secretary, and S. F. Baird, secretary of

15 J. J. Stevenson to O. C. Marsh, March 15, 20, 1878, Marsh Papers.

16 U. S., *Statutes at Large*, XX (Washington, 1877-1879), 230.

17 U. S., *Congressional Record*, 45th Cong., 3rd Sess., February 12, 1879, p. 1204.

the Smithsonian Institution, disliked the controversial subject. Baird also argued that under the constitution of the academy the vice-president could not act in place of the president. But Marsh organized a Special Committee on Scientific Surveys of seven members, with himself as chairman, to consider the problem and to report to a general meeting of the academy in New York City in November.[18]

Before selecting this special committee, Marsh clarified his own ideas about a solution. King was his scientific adviser,[19] and Simon Newcomb, director of the Naval Observatory, kept him informed of Washington opinion. King advised two civilian surveys, one for economic geology, the other for topographical mapping. There was no question in Marsh's mind about the civilian control of economic geology, but he hesitated on the second civilian survey, since both Hewitt and Humphreys, whom he also consulted, were urging a large role for the military in topographical mapping. The existence of a civilian mapping agency—the Coast and Geodetic Survey within the Treasury Department already engaged in plotting a belt of astronomically determined positions across the continent—impressed him. When Newcomb reported from Washington that C. P. Patterson, superintendent of the Coast and Geodetic Survey, was receptive to new responsibilities, Marsh adopted King's view.

Patterson was skeptical, however, that anything could be accomplished. He felt the opposition of the engineers would be powerful enough to kill legislation. Patterson predicted

18 J. E. Hilgard to O. C. Marsh, June 19, 1878, J. J. Stevenson to O. C. Marsh, July 17, 1878, Marsh Papers. The special committee could, according to the constitution of the academy, communicate directly with Congress, but Marsh "thought it better to have the report submitted . . . to the Academy before transmission." O. C. Marsh to the Speaker of the House of Representatives, April 15, 1879, House Misc. Doc. No. 7, 46th Cong., 1st Sess., 7.

19 Alexander Agassiz to C. P. Patterson, November 8, 1878, Records of the Coast and Geodetic Survey, Superintendent's File, No. 423, Miscellaneous Correspondence, A-K, 1878, U.S. National Archives. In this letter Agassiz acknowledged King's service to the academy committee.

trouble within the next decade as his men completed mapping the coastline and were ready to go elsewhere; "the great fight would therefore be between the civil and the military for the conduct of these interior surveys."[20]

Marsh wanted unanimous approval on his plan for civilian-controlled surveys, and to obtain this unanimity he was willing to deprive the military of fair representation on the committee. Newcomb was inclined to put down either General Humphreys or M. C. Meigs, quartermaster-general during the Civil War, not entertaining the dread of a minority report. But he readily admitted that Humphreys was out of the question if a dissenting opinion must be avoided. Meigs, he thought, might go along with the majority. To find out, he paid a call on the distinguished veteran and reported back that Meigs seemed to think the army engineers should conduct the surveys.[21] Marsh, therefore, dismissed the quartermaster-general as a possibility. The nearest he came to recognizing the military was the appointment of W. P. Trowbridge, a professor of engineering at the Columbia School of Mines, a West Point graduate, and for several years a member of the Corps of Engineers.

Another selection by Marsh for the committee was Alexander Agassiz, a zoologist and son of Louis, who opposed natural history in public surveys. He had recently warned Hayden that Congress would examine very closely his publications in that field. The study of biology, Agassiz thought, had killed the state surveys of Massachusetts, New York, Michigan, and others. Agassiz, also a successful businessman, had taken badly managed copper properties in northern Michigan and had made them very profitable. Since the academy had been asked to consider the surveys of the General Land Office, Marsh wanted some informed person on the committee, and Agassiz' experience with mineral lands recommended him.

The committee, assembled by October, included Trow-

20 Simon Newcomb to O. C. Marsh, October 5, 1878, Marsh Papers.
21 *Ibid.* Newcomb proposed Humphreys as chairman of the committee.

bridge, Agassiz, Newcomb, and a trio of geologists—J. D. Dana, W. B. Rogers, and J. S. Newberry—all of whom had been in public service. Dana had served as far back as the 1840's with the Wilkes Expedition; Rogers had worked in Virginia; and Newberry had been first with War Department parties and then director of a survey in Ohio.

With the formation of the committee Powell began to influence the plans for a united survey. He sent copies of his *Lands of the Arid Region* to members, who borrowed from it for the academy plan. When Marsh asked for written opinions from the field protagonists, Powell submitted a long, comprehensive communication. It had no direct influence on the proceedings of the committee, which had met and drawn up recommendations before Powell, Wheeler, and Hayden could return from the West to prepare replies, yet his answer was hailed as the best exposition of the academy plan. Friendly congressmen quoted him, and Hewitt, after a reading, came over completely to the side of the civilian scientists.

Powell's letter rationalized the proposed reduction of government science. Some persons on the committee, such as Agassiz, believed in less activity as a matter of principle; others, guided by expediency, hoped to make economy of expenditure the lure for cost-conscious congressmen like Atkins and James A. Garfield, who had shown continued uneasiness about different parties working in the same area. Powell urged that "the endowment of science by governments . . . be very limited and scrupulously confined" because "the efforts and energies of individuals acting from no other stimulus than the love of science" brought better results than government patronage. Sometimes, however, the magnitude and expense of scientific undertakings put them beyond the reach of individual enterprise. Then the state could intervene, after making sure that the investigations satisfied democratic and utilitarian requirements. In a popular government, science must show results "for the immediate use and wants of all classes"; any survey valuable chiefly for "abstract science" must always be "weak and have an uncertain tenure of existence."[22] Geology was above reproach, Powell claimed, because it had an alliance with the mining industry, and its mapping projects were obviously too large for individual management. Studies in topography and hydrology, producing land classification maps, served the important settler-farmer class. Neither botany nor zoology could claim any such economic connection, and thousands of individual scientists already were fruitfully engaged in those fields, making government research unnecessary. Powell made an exception for special inquiries intimately affecting the national welfare; the government might have to take quick and expensive action to control the cotton worm and the locust or to investigate the growth and production of forests.

The formal action of the National Academy was swift and quiet. On November 6 the special committee went before the academy at a session during the semiannual meeting in New York. Thirty-five scientists listened to a report which made two primary recommendations. First, the committee advised that Congress establish within the Department of the Interior an independent and single organization to be known as the United States Geological Survey, which would be charged with the study of the geological structure and economic resources of the public domain. Second, they recommended that there be in the same department a U. S. Coast and Interior Survey. This unit (essentially the existing Coast Survey) would embrace all the mapping in the public domain, whether for latitude and longitude, for representing earth features, or for demarcation of any area as a prelude to its sale.

Under this recommendation geodesy, topography, and land parceling would come under one director. Neither new bureau would exercise all its powers immediately, as the committee proposed that a commission appointed by Congress submit within a year a standard for classifying and valuing the public

22 J. W. Powell to Carl Schurz, November 1, 1878, U. S., House Misc. Doc. No. 5, 45th Cong., 3rd Sess., 23-25.

lands and a system of land parceling survey. The report specifically abolished the Hayden, Powell, and Wheeler surveys
and the mapping by the General Land Office. Other sciences
were passed over, except for paleontology which was described
as "necessarily connected" with geology.[23]

Discussion went on for several hours at the session of the
academy, with half of the scientists speaking up. No valid
point seems to have been made against the report. Humphreys,
on leave of absence from the corps since July, did not attend.
Meigs and H. L. Abbot, the two most prominent engineers
present, consented. The vote in favor was 33 to 1, with E. D.
Cope casting the only negative vote.

For a time the same steady progress went on outside the
academy. On November 9 Marsh was in Washington to see
ranking officials. President Hayes, "so far as he had the plan
before him," Secretaries Carl Schurz and John Sherman of the
Departments of the Interior and the Treasury, W. T. Sherman
who commanded the U. S. Army, and Superintendent Patterson of the Coast Survey, all gave their approval. Everywhere
in scientific circles Marsh heard favorable comment. Hilgard
and Baird, who earlier had been so skeptical about the con-
gressionally imposed task, now agreed to the unified survey.
Powell, who was not a member of the academy, said he was
satisfied.

On November 14, a sudden controversy developed when
Humphreys resigned from the National Academy of Sciences
in protest against its report, resuming at the same time his
post with the Corps of Engineers. His resignation was the
signal for the military to rally forces against the recommendation. General C. B. Comstock, who was engaged in surveys in
the Great Lakes region, joined immediately. J. G. Parke, a
Civil War corps commander, who had "served almost contin-
uously from 1849 to 1861 on Explorations and Surveys in our
Western Territories," wrote indignantly that the report was

[23] "A Report on the Surveys of the Territories," *ibid.*, 2-5.

the "culmination of a scheme which had been on foot for
several years past by parties of different interests to turn us
out of our Territory, and appropriate it to their own uses and
aggrandizement."[24] Marsh soon heard from Patterson that the
engineers were opposed to the academy's report. The army
scientists came together easily, inspired by a deep sense of
injustice at their exclusion from the academy committee.

Humphreys' resignation was news, and the Washington
press carried the story with a candid account of the events
leading to the general's action. Some important out-of-town
newspapers, such as the Boston *Daily Advertiser* and the Cincinnati *Commercial Gazette,* were hostile. H. V. N. Boynton,
the Washington correspondent for the *Gazette,* leveled charges
of adroit management and secret action against the academy.

Civilian scientists countered with their own publicity and
united against Humphreys' criticisms. A. G. Wetherby, professor of geology and zoology at the University of Cincinnati,
and O. W. Gibbs, chemist at Harvard College, both wrote suggesting that the support of influential newspapers be sought
for the academy's position. A very active tactician, Powell
asked Newberry of Columbia to meet with Stevenson of New
York University, who had been heard to say that the engineers
should have complete charge of western surveys. When Patterson, worrying about newspaper charges, said that General
Humphreys had been treated badly in not having a place on
the academy committee, Powell sought to reassure the superintendent: "Cannot Pierce and Trowbridge influence him?"
he asked King.[25]

One intellectual skirmish between the two groups of scientists began with a sharp attack by Humphreys and Comstock
on the Coast Survey. The report of the academy had not spe-

24 J. G. Parke to O. C. Marsh, December 5, 1878, Marsh Papers.
25 J. W. Powell to Clarence King, November 29, 1878, Rocky Mountain
Region Survey, Letters Sent, 1878. Evidently Powell meant Benjamin Peirce,
former superintendent of the Coast Survey.
C. P. Patterson to O. C. Marsh, November 22, 1878, Marsh Papers.

cifically advised that organization on its mapping methods—
how many points to determine astronomically in a unit area,
what scale to use, how to represent physical features, and so
forth. The two generals criticized this omission and then, interpreting the past performance of the Coast Survey, predicted
that the Coast Survey would map the public domain at a rate
of $584 per square mile and at a cost of half a billion dollars,
a fantastic figure in the days when annual government expenditures had yet to reach the billion dollar level.

The generals retracted somewhat when Superintendent Patterson replied that their calculations included the Civil War
when little or no mapping was done, although the Coast
Survey was still paying salaries. The revised figure was $403
per square mile, still very high. Patterson and Powell said that
the cost of mapping varied with the degree of refinement, that
no one was proposing to extend into the interior the typical
detail of coastline maps, and that congressional discretion was
the ultimate security against huge expenditures. Less than a
week after Humphreys' first letter, King was calling it "a very
weak document which has already helped us."[26] He and the
others no longer had to worry whether or not Patterson would
identify himself publicly with the general.

After the report of the academy had been made part of the
Legislative, Executive, and Judicial Appropriation Bill, the
fight over the survey moved to the House of Representatives.
Simon Newcomb predicted swift passage. King looked for a
"lively fight"; "Wheeler, Genl Comstock of the Engineers and
Humphreys are working, and the Land Rings are rampant,"
he explained.[27] On February 10, 1879, in committee of the

26 Clarence King to O. C. Marsh, January 16, 1879, *ibid*.

27 *Ibid*. W. E. Merrill, the engineer for the canalization of the Ohio
River, wrote to several representatives, renewing the discussion about
costs, the length of service by the army, and the superiority of its surveying. Copy of a letter by W. E. Merrill, February 5, 1879, Rocky Mountain
Region Survey, Letters Received, 1879, M-Z, 31-32.

whole, the House came to the sections recommended by the academy. And for two days four representatives urged their adoption: Hewitt, Atkins, Garfield, and P. D. Wigginton of California.

Atkins and Wigginton made it possible for Powell to confront Congress with some of his ideas from *Lands of the Arid Region*. Wigginton borrowed Powell's categories of irrigable, timber, and pasturage lands to summarize the physical facts, which required, he said, a radical change in the laws and system of survey. He was concerned that there was no genuine land classification, that the rectangular system of parceling lacked flexibility, that the lines run were often unnecessary and always unscientific (no latitude, longitude, or altitude), and that the surveying was spotty—primarily because 16 different surveyors-general farmed out work to private persons. Atkins raised the peril of a few favored capitalists dominating a region because they controlled the water rights, and Wigginton named five percent as the redeemable agricultural total.

Garfield's task was to present the plan of the academy as an economy measure and to acquaint Congress with the Agassiz-Powell thesis of limited government in science. Garfield argued that science, like religion, should be controlled by the people, rather than by either the national or the state government. Except for one clause in the Constitution authorizing Congress to grant copyrights and patents, the founding fathers reserved the field of science for voluntary, individual action. After stressing the government's duty to study scientifically the character and quality of the public lands, Garfield asked for consolidation of the surveys to avoid wasting money, duplicating work, and making the name of science ridiculous in the United States.

The climax of the two-day debate was the hour-long oration by Hewitt on February 11. With the entire House listening, the congressman from New York City argued eloquently for his conception of a geological survey, which resembled King's and inspired the new bureau. Still excited by his own conversion, Hewitt wanted civilians in charge of the Survey. Taking his cue from Powell, he rejected the military engineers as representative of a foreign tradition. Soldiers were the scientists in Europe, because Europe was a battlefield, "and through the long ages, unhappily, war has largely filled the measure of its experience." But in America the civilian scientist was the leader. *"Cedent arma togae,"* he declaimed.

These civilian scientists studied economic geology, an activity as noble and imperative for the future of the United States as constitution making had been for its past. Deserting the cautious attitude of Wigginton and Powell toward natural resources, Hewitt gave a 15-minute peroration on the material abundance of the continent. Its economic prospect filled him with wonder and praise: the vast coalfields in three mountain systems, the soils of the Mississippi Valley (deep, fertile, and self-renewing), the precious metals, and the exhaustless iron ores, which spreading so far caused Hewitt to exclaim with Macbeth, "What! will the line stretch out to the crack of doom? . . . I'll see no more." These riches provided for every aspiration of man. They were the origin of measureless values which sprang into being "at the touch of modern industry" and were incorporated into "the enduring structure of human society." Hewitt urged the nation to preserve civil liberty unharmed and to adopt such surveys as would prevent the waste of mineral resources and clear the way for progress and civilization. Hailing the great American republic, he cried, *"Esto perpetua,"* and sat down amid tremendous applause.[28]

The cosmic mood of the House gradually changed into discontent and even derision, as representatives from the states and territories with public lands entered the debate. Almost to a man they fought those features of the academy's plan which abolished the office of surveyor-general and sought bet-

[28] U. S., *Congressional Record*, 45th Cong., 3rd Sess., February 11, 1879, pp. 1203, 1204, 1207.

ter ways to map than by meridians, parallels, and section lines which had no astronomical foundation. Martin Maginnis of Montana wanted to know who except a few scientists in Washington would eliminate the surveyor-general's office. The land system should be left strictly alone. It was so plain and simple, said Maginnis, that any 40 acres could be described in a dozen words. According to T. M. Patterson of Colorado, American prosperity was founded upon it. Several legislatures conveyed their displeasure, as did Commissioner J. A. Williamson of the General Land Office. All the protests went back to grassroots sentiment in Kansas and other western states or territories that the movement toward consolidation threatened existing surveys and, therefore, actual or potential property rights.[29]

Powell got nowhere, then, trying to make science (topography and hydrology) popular by injecting it into western land practice. To western agrarians such knowledge seemed at best ornamental or irrelevant, at worst an irritating falsehood. Amid laughter, D. C. Haskell of Kansas said he was quite willing to have scientists dig fossils, and hunt bugs, and discover the rotundity of the earth. But, said Maginnis, let them keep their hands off the settler, who only wanted to know whether his 80 or 160 acres fell within the four corners of his claim, not "whether the 'bulge of the earth' has removed him any farther than his neighbor Jones from the region of the central fire." Patterson of Colorado reacted to the realism of Powell by calling him a "charlatan," who underestimated western land and water resources.[30]

[29] E. W. Ayres to J. W. Powell, January 20, 1879, Rocky Mountain Region Survey, Letters Received, 1879.

[30] These comments are recorded in U.S., *Congressional Record*, 45th Cong., 3rd Sess., February 11, 1879, p. 1202; Appendix, 217, 220-21.

"The people on the frontier," said territorial representative S. B. Elkins of New Mexico in 1877, "care nothing about geodetic points, isothermal lines, and the Silurian system; they want homes, farms, and mines, and therefore desire the public domain surveyed . . . and do not want ornamental and scientific surveys." *Ibid.*, 44th Cong., 2nd Sess., February 21, 1877, p. 1793.

Simultaneously, the agrarian critics favored unification of geological studies and their service to the mining industry, except for three or four who supported the army engineers. On the evening of February 18, H. F. Page of California submitted an amendment exempting the land surveys from the general reorganization. The House adopted Page's proposal, 98 to 70. The Coast and Interior Survey now managed all surveys concerning position and mensuration of the coast and interior, except the land surveys. The other institutional changes still remained—the creation of the U. S. Geological Survey, the abolition of the Wheeler, Hayden, and Powell surveys, and the formation of a commission on the public lands. On February 25 the entire Legislative, Executive, and Judicial Appropriation Bill passed the House, which already had sent on to the Senate the Sundry Civil Appropriation Bill authorizing the director of the new Survey to spend $100,000 the first year.[31]

For sponsors in the House the period of formal presentation and public discussion was now over. Hewitt and Atkins decided against pressing ahead in the Senate. Either they thought there had been enough of a legislative test or that time was too short, as it was only a week before the end of the session.

The decision not to press for a favorable vote in the Senate gave Hayden his best opportunity during the legislative proceedings. His autumn letter to Marsh and the special committee revealed the determination to maneuver so that regardless of the outcome he would remain head of a territorial survey. Hayden opposed any great, comprehensive plan, but thought that, if there were to be one organization, then by merit, seniority, and public acclaim he deserved to be its leader. He claimed that the surveys of Wheeler, Powell, and King grew out of his survey and were successful insofar as they imitated its methods and organization.

Necessarily, Hayden's campaign was two-faced. He bowed

[31] For the legislation as it went to the Senate see U. S., *Congressional Record*, 45th Cong., 3rd Sess., February 18, 1879, p. 2182.

before the initial momentum of the academy plan, neither speaking nor voting against it at the November meeting in New York. Between the gathering forces of the civilians and the military he had no real choice. Outwardly he always favored the developing legislation. Covertly and indirectly, however, he fought against consolidation, knowing well that the reform scientists did not have him in mind for the directorship. His chief ally was E. D. Cope, who alone had voted negatively in the academy.

In January, Cope praised the multiple surveys west of the Mississippi in an editorial in his magazine the *American Naturalist*. Cope probably wrote the anonymous letter which touched off a skirmish during the House debate in February. Haskell of Kansas, who was for Hayden, read from a letter by "a member of the National Academy," which asserted that some of the academy were antagonistic to its plan and gave several names: Baird of the Smithsonian, Peter Lesley, the geologist, Joseph Leidy, the naturalist, and Arnold Guyot, the geographer. The letter also said that the proponents "have a scheme for placing a graduate of one of their colleges in the single position which is to represent those now filled by Hayden, Wheeler, and others." A rapid fire exchange followed, with three or four representatives insisting that the entire letter be read and its origin disclosed. Haskell refused, although it was brought out that the author lived in Pennsylvania.

"Mr. SPARKS. The gentleman ought not to read from a letter that he dare not give the name of the author of, and the whole of which he dare not read.

"Mr. HASKELL walked across the floor to Mr. SPARKS, and (holding up the letter to him) said: There is the name.

"Mr. SPARKS. I do not want to pry into your secrets. The gentleman ought to give the name of the author."[32]

When the two appropriation bills creating and financing

32 U. S., *Congressional Record,* 45th Cong., 3rd Sess., February 18, 1879, p. 1560.

the Geological Survey came to the Senate, Hayden showed his political prowess. On February 28 Senators A. A. Sargent of California and William Windom of Minnesota, representing the committee on appropriations, moved that the clause in the Sundry Civil Appropriation Bill granting $100,000 to the new bureau be changed to read: "For the expenses of the Geological and Geographical Survey of the Territories . . . $100,000";[33] in other words, the Hayden survey should receive the money intended by the House for the Geological Survey. Senator Sargent spoke frankly. During the previous session, Congress had "improvidently authorized a body called the Academy of Sciences" to report upon the western surveys. That academy replied with "a caricature on the whole subject," offering a new and expensive survey to replace all current operations. The committee on appropriations of the Senate placed no faith in the proposed change, such was its members' admiration for Hayden. The Senate approved the amendment, refused $20,000 to complete the Powell survey, granting it instead to Hayden, allocated $20,000 to wind up the Wheeler survey, and passed on to other business. The next day, March 1, the same committee moved to strike out the section in the Legislative, Executive, and Judicial Appropriation Bill, voted by the House on February 18, which established the Coast and Interior Survey and the U. S. Geological Survey, organized the commission on the public lands, and abolished the existing organizations. The Senate agreed without comment. Legislation sponsoring the academy plan had now been transformed to Hayden's advantage, and there was only one working day left of the Forty-fifth Congress.

On that day, March 3, Hewitt and Atkins made their successful counterattack in behalf of the academy measure. They were on the conference committee, which was meeting to reconcile differences in the two appropriation bills passed by the House and the Senate. In this committee Hewitt and

[33] *Ibid.*, February 28, 1879, p. 2084.

Atkins restored to the Sundry Civil Appropriation Bill the section deleted by the Senate from the Legislative, Executive, and Judicial Appropriation Bill, which established the Geological Survey, wiped out the current western surveys, and authorized a commission on the public lands. Of course the appropriation of funds in the same bill, which the Senate had transferred to Hayden, was returned to the new bureau. No doubt Hewitt and Atkins were aided in their coup by Senator H. G. Davis of West Virginia, a member of the conference committee. Davis, like Hewitt, was fascinated by the prospect of vast natural resources, which he personally exploited through railroads and mines that he owned in the Appalachian region.

That evening, three hours before adjournment, the Senate had to decide whether it would accept in the Sundry Civil Bill what it had rejected emphatically two days before in the Legislative, Executive, and Judicial Appropriation Bill. G. F. Edmunds of Vermont quickly charged a wide departure from the authority of a conference committee, because it had initiated new legislation. He urged the Senate not to frighten at the prospect of losing the Sundry Civil Bill. A. E. Burnside of Rhode Island said it was "an insult to the intelligence and independence of this body to ask them to act upon this amendment to-night, changing the whole system of surveys at the dictation of a subcommittee of the House."[34] J. B. Beck of Kentucky declared that the committee on appropriations had received the reform measure—five printed pages of the Legislative, Executive, and Judicial Bill—so late in the session that it had had no opportunity to study it. Windom of the conference committee confessed to some misgivings about the parliamentary propriety of what had been done, but said there was no doubt of the bill's desirability. S. W. Dorsey of Arkansas, also one of the managers for the Senate, wondered if any three other members could have done better, considering

34 *Ibid.*, March 3, 1879, p. 2302.

that the Sundry Civil Bill affected so many different interests and contained so many amendments. He predicted failure for the entire bill if the Senate dissented, as there was no time before noon of the next day for the conference committee to meet again.

By a vote of 35 to 24 the Senate concurred in the report of the committee of conferences. Earlier in the day the House had consented, 148 to 107. President Hayes' signature making the Sundry Civil Bill a law and creating the Geological Survey was appended the same evening of March 3.[35]

Senator Windom had promised peace if the bill creating the Survey passed, but there was no peace after March 3, despite the elimination of the Corps of Engineers. The competition grew fiercer and more personal, shifting now to the Executive Mansion, as the rival candidates, King and Hayden, sought the directorship of the new Survey. Powell renounced "all claim or desire or effort to be head of a united survey."[36]

Hayden's advantage was his seniority in western science and his scientific reputation. Arnold Guyot, the geographer at

[35] U. S., *Statutes at Large,* XX (1877-1879), 394-95.
"For the salary of the Director of the Geological Survey, which office is hereby established, under the Interior Department, who shall be appointed by the President by and with the advice and consent of the Senate, six thousand dollars: *Provided,* That this officer shall have the direction of the Geological Survey, and the classification of the public lands and examination of the Geological Structure, mineral resources and products of the national domain. And that the Director and members of the Geological Survey shall have no personal or private interests in the lands or mineral wealth of the region under survey, and shall execute no surveys or examinations for private parties or corporations"; [the Hayden, Powell and Wheeler surveys are discontinued]. "And all collections of rocks, minerals, soils, fossils, and objects of natural history, Archaeology, and ethnology, made by the Coast and Interior Survey, the Geological Survey, or by any other parties for the Government of the United States, when no longer needed for investigations in progress shall be deposited in the National Museum."
[36] Copy of a letter from C. E. Dutton to A. G. Wetherby, November 21, 1878, Rocky Mountain Region Survey, Letters Received, 1878, A-I, 139-45.

Princeton, argued that Hayden already headed the Geological Survey and that "justice, & the honor of the country, require that . . . long, tried & efficient services . . . should not be rewarded by a removal without cause."[37] Because Hayden had made his survey a publishing house for research in botany, zoology, and paleontology, he was better known than King among English and American scientists. Also, the Colorado atlas had spread his fame in Europe. Representing a broad spectrum of intellectual interests on Capitol Hill, where he went so often, he was the only scientist most congressmen knew.

King's strength was his special suitability for the kind of survey which had been created. According to Gardiner, he was "the only Government Geologist who is an educated and experienced mining engineer . . . [and] I judge that the practical application of geology, particularly to Mining, is to be of paramount importance in the proposed survey."[38] "Few American geologists," wrote Gilbert, "have undertaken so wide a range of theoretic and economic studies, and none have acquitted themselves with greater credit."[39] R. W. Raymond and five "merchants" of New York City approved of King. Raymond, who used the stationery of Cooper, Hewitt, and Company, identified himself as editor of the *Engineering and Mining Journal,* as executive officer of the American Institute of Mining Engineers, and as former U. S. Commissioner of Mining Statistics. The five merchants, among them W. E. Dodge, Jr., acknowledged their interest "in the development of the mining and other natural resources of the United States."[40]

[37] Arnold Guyot to O. C. Marsh, March 14, 1879, Marsh Papers.

[38] J. T. Gardiner, Director, New York State Survey, to R. B. Hayes, January 18, 1879, Rutherford B. Hayes Papers, Hayes Memorial Library.

[39] G. K. Gilbert to R. B. Hayes, March 5, 1879, *ibid.*

[40] Merchants of the City of New York to R. B. Hayes, March 15, 1879, *ibid.* W. E. Dodge, Jr., was a partner in Phelps, Dodge & Company, dealers in copper and other metals.

Hayden took the initiative in campaigning for presidential support. In much the same way as he had intrigued to defeat the legislation establishing the Survey, he now collected pledges promising him the directorship. The faculties of Princeton College and the University of Minnesota signed for him. Among those speaking to President Hayes in Hayden's behalf were Guyot, Cope, and Alexander Winchell, geologist at the University of Michigan.

This activity caused Stevenson to warn Marsh as early as December that "Hayden has already made a long stride towards the position and unless something be done speedily he will be the man and nothing short of omnipotence can prevent it."[41] Toward the end of February, when the feeling was strong in Washington that Hayden would win, Powell led a renewed drive for King testimonials. As his "chief credential," King offered a glowing statement from President Noah Porter of Yale College, President Emeritus T. D. Woolsey, and a dozen professors.[42] Powell and Newcomb visited the White House, urging Garfield, Newberry, Noah Porter, and W. B. Rogers to do likewise.

Some of the oral and written communications were intended to hurt rather than to help. Hayden's supporters denounced the moneymaking ventures of King in ranching and mining while he was chief of the Exploration of the Fortieth Parallel. He also had accepted $7,500 for a report on a mine owned by Senator Logan of Illinois.[43]

[41] J. J. Stevenson to O. C. Marsh, December 20, 1878, Marsh Papers.

[42] Clarence King to O. C. Marsh, January 2, 1879, Marsh Papers; Officers and Professors of the Yale Faculty to his Excellency, the President of the United States, January 10, 1879, Hayes Papers.

[43] Diary of Alexander Winchell, March 13-24, 1879, Michigan State Historical Society.

Hayden told Joseph Leidy, professor of anatomy and paleontologist at the University of Pennsylvania, that King was gathering most of the New England scientists on his side and that Marsh was claiming the appointment for "the two oldest colleges in the land." F. V. Hayden to Joseph Leidy, February 4, March 5, 1879, Joseph Leidy Papers, Philadelphia Academy of Natural Sciences.

When Garfield was preparing to see President Hayes, Powell mailed the congressman a lengthy statement on Hayden and his science, calling him "a charlatan who has bought his way to fame with Government money and unlimited access to the Government Printing Office."[44]

If the Harvard community never recommended King, it may have been just as helpful by censuring Hayden. President Charles W. Eliot, communicating with President Hayes, named J. D. Whitney of Harvard as the best man for the directorship. He also praised King, the "pupil and subordinate of Professor Whitney," but for Hayden he had only abuse: "I have often heard his ignorance, his scientific incapacity, and his low habits when in camp, commented on with aversion and mortification. He has never shown that he is himself either a geologist, a topographer, a botanist, or a zoologist."[45]

During March, President Hayes sifted the materials which months of intense activity had placed before him. He found more eminence among geologists following King than among those favoring Hayden, though two of the foremost, Dana and Whitney, refused to declare for either one.[46] Thinking of his administration as moral and reform-minded, in contrast to Grant's, Hayes questioned Powell on Hayden's methods in securing appropriations. Both Powell and Garfield cited the brief fight against the locust in the 1870's that was waged by the U. S. Entomological Commission. When money was first sought in the House, Hayden defeated the project by saying that it would be a new survey. In the Senate westerners

Hayden informed J. L. LeConte, the entomologist, that Marsh and Agassiz were wealthy and could get along without government aid, "but all are not so situated." F. V. Hayden to J. L. LeConte, February 27, 1879, John Lawrence LeConte Papers, American Philosophical Society.

44 J. W. Powell to James A. Garfield, March 7, 1879, Rocky Mountain Region Survey, Letters Sent, 1879.

45 C. W. Eliot to R. B. Hayes, February 28, 1879, Hayes Papers.

46 J. D. Dana to Clarence King, January 7, 1879, Hayes Papers. J. D. Whitney to S. F. Emmons, January 8, 1879, Emmons Papers.

pushed the bill so earnestly that Hayden and James Stevenson, the ethnologist, who was his executive aide, asked Senator Sargent to place the commission under their jurisdiction.
Afterward, Hayden informed the members of the commission
that "it had come to his knowledge that the appropriation
was about to be refused and in order to save it he had permitted it to be tacked to his own appropriation."[47] Ultimately,
the President put his trust in two persons, Carl Schurz, Secretary of the Interior, and Newberry, who had been state geologist in Ohio when Hayes was governor. Both were friendly
to King and hostile to Hayden. On March 21 the President
sent the name of King to the Senate, and on April 3 King
became the first director of the U. S. Geological Survey.

There is a central theme behind what happened to public
science and scientists in 1879, behind the events which established the Survey and determined its leadership. This theme
was the post-Civil War movement to exploit natural resources.
It was strong enough to establish the primacy of economic
geology, and it deemphasized military topographical surveys,
land reform, and general information. These other surveys,
although themselves expressions of broad social forces, could
not prevail against this materialistic current. In the contest
for the directorship the same overpowering influence of the
acquisitive spirit was less apparent. Many who had applauded
Hewitt's plea for economic advancement in the mining industry as the measure of a scientific survey supported the general geologist Hayden. But even in this more complicated
situation the economic geologist King emerged victorious.

The pressure in 1879 for limited science was not absolute.
Hayden and Gilbert joined the new organization (along with
Emmons and Arnold Hague from the Exploration of the
Fortieth Parallel).[48] A few topographers were needed imme-

[47] J. W. Powell to James A. Garfield, March 7, 1879, Rocky Mountain
Region Survey, Letters Sent, 1879.

[48] Powell became director of the Bureau of Ethnology. He also joined
and influenced the commission on the public lands, but Congress did
nothing about its many findings.

diately, and a young paleontologist, C. D. Walcott, was hired the first summer. Furthermore, the reaction against multiple science was only temporary. During the 1880's the Geological Survey reinstituted projects of the former western surveys and thus maintained the continuity of science.

Chapter Three

A BUREAU OF MINES AND MINING

The Geological Survey was created primarily to achieve an immediate economic objective. Director King was enforcing the central purpose of the founding when he ordered several of his staff into the mining centers of western America. The "incomparable" Comstock Lode and the "wonderful" silver deposits at Leadville, Colorado, and Eureka, Nevada, were his initial locations.[1] The gold fields of California also had a high priority. King imagined his scientists moving on from these places to other major districts, increasing the literature of mining geology. And after a decade, someone, perhaps King himself, could formulate a general theory as to the origin and formation of ore deposits.

King's first step in organizing the program of the Geological Survey was the establishment of the division of the Rocky Mountains with its headquarters at Denver with Emmons in charge. Starting in Colorado, Emmons was to prepare monographs on the Leadville region, the mining districts on the waters of Clear Creek, and the Wet Mountain Valley districts. These several projects would train younger geologists, who, after their apprenticeship, could be dispatched to mining districts in New Mexico, Wyoming, the Dakotas, and Montana for independent investigations. The expanding professional force would allow accumulation of knowledge at an ever faster pace and bring nearer the time when sound theorizing could begin. The location of regional headquarters at Denver, only a day's journey from the mining centers of Colorado, demonstrated

King's intention to make the new bureau a more effective and persistent force in mining communities than the parent surveys, which usually had operated as annual summer expeditions out of Washington. Geologists could move easily between field and office; they could make immediate use of good company maps in their examination of mines, since copying facilities were nearby. A laboratory at Denver permitted chemical tests while the field work was in progress, and scientists could make quick collection of rock supplies if some material proved of unexpected interest upon examination.

Taking seriously the commitment of the Survey to practical geology, Emmons began his work with a statement on the geological and mining history of Leadville. Although his account has been modified by later research, his exposition of the complex effects of faulting, folding, erosion, and glacial activity since the end of the Cretaceous period in the Leadville area remains generally valid. Chopping through the glacial mantle or broken bedrock in any piece of available territory, the miners had uncovered a number of rich concentrations. More often this haphazard prospecting was a failure. "The hills for miles around Leadville," Emmons wrote, "are literally honeycombed with shafts and tunnels, probably the greater number of which are so situated that either it would be geologically impossible for them to reach the ore-bearing bed, or it would be found at such depths as . . . to render it practically worthless when reached."[2] To put mineral exploration on a scientific footing, he proposed maps of all the dif-

[1] Clarence King to Carl Schurz, May 14, 1879, Carl Schurz Papers, Library of Congress.

[2] S. F. Emmons to Clarence King, October 10, 1880, *First Annual Report of the U. S. Geological Survey* (Washington, 1880), 21. These documents are hereinafter cited as U.S.G.S. *First Annual Report,* U.S.G.S. *Second Annual Report,* and so forth. Later exploration at Leadville showed that there was another important ore-bearing bed. S. F. Emmons, J. D. Irving, and G. F. Loughlin, *Geology and Ore Deposits of the Leadville District, Colorado,* Geological Survey Professional Paper No. 148 (Washington, 1927), 32.

ferent sedimentary and igneous rocks, geological sections across Leadville's Mosquito Range (for a picture of interior structure), and diagrams of the ore-bearing horizons on the surface and underground. Should the miners use this scientific reasoning successfully, the division of the Rocky Mountains would be demonstrating the utility of geology and realizing the primary objective of the new Survey.

To the Comstock Lode, the richest of all American silver-gold lodes, King sent George Ferdinand Becker, a graduate of the Royal School of Mines in Berlin, who wanted to do lithological studies. Becker was impressed with the great variety of rocks at the Comstock and the diversity of opinion among his predecessors as to their nature and age. He was pleased with the advantage which "current microscopical determinations" gave him, "a check and guide at the command of none of the geologists who have hitherto reported upon the lode."[3] He also wanted to explain the origin of the intense heat in the lode; air and water were consistently over 100° F.

Becker visited the Sutro Tunnel continually, meeting obstacles which frustrated even the most modern skills: "the rocks are in great part decomposed beyond recognition," he wrote, "and there are thousands of feet where candles burn so dimly in the bad air that one can scarcely see where to step. The air is hot and foul, and the hind and mule manure often ankle deep. Deciding from foot to foot on complicated and decomposed rocks under these conditions is very hard work, and I have spent from six to eight hours at it day after day with very small results."[4]

[3] G. F. Becker to Clarence King, October 10, 1880, U.S.G.S. *First Annual Report*, 40. Becker is referring to the use of the microscope and thin rock sections for studying the mineral and chemical nature of matter. This technique was developed after the middle of the century. See G. F. Becker, *Geology of the Comstock Lode and the Washoe District* (Washington, 1882), 32-33.

[4] G. F. Becker to Clarence King, September 1, 1880, U. S. Geological Survey, Letters Received, 1880. The Sutro Tunnel was the project, completed in 1878, to help exploit the Comstock mines more effectively by lessening the water hazard.

One unusual part of King's program at Virginia City and the Comstock Lode was a historical monograph. With the desire to celebrate American mining, King thought that no place would be more fitting than where some of the best miners in America had received their training, where $300 million of silver and gold had been extracted, and where events had affected national legislation. The resulting monograph by Eliot Lord, *Comstock Mining and Miners,* was the epic of an industry, the dramatic story about the "rush to Washoe," the endless litigation over possession and ownership, the condition and conflict of labor, and, above all, "how, in the course of only twenty years, the deepest and most productive silver mines in the world were excavated in a gangue of crumbling rock, in spite of a constant influx of water and an unprecedented influx of heat."[5]

The Survey went beyond geology to voice criticism of practices in American mining. The geologists disliked the speculation, fictitious prosperity, dishonesty, and waste which had characterized mining. Emmons reported that "the occupation of mining, its search after the unseen and unknown, its sudden and unlooked-for vicissitudes, the supposed importance of keeping up an excitement in order to attract capital, have in many cases so biased the moral sense of otherwise honest men that they seem to consider it a duty to themselves and their community in which they live to exaggerate the production or value of any mining property."[6] King believed that events had transformed the Comstock Lode into a colossal stock lottery.[7]

The Survey saw the ideal mining community as more static and conservative. Members should make their money, like Europeans, in small and stable profits, not relying on huge

5 *Comstock Mining and Miners* (Washington, 1883), ix. Lord (1851-1928) was a newspaperman in Boston and New York.

6 S. F. Emmons to Clarence King, October 10, 1880, U.S.G.S. *First Annual Report,* 63.

7 "Introductory Remarks," in S. F. Emmons and G. F. Becker, *Statistics and Technology of the Precious Metals* (Washington, 1885), xiii.

speculative returns as Americans had in the past. Attention should go to details of expense and minute metallurgical savings, with the Geological Survey providing technical and scientific information. Emmons saw a return to "the old time ideas of the true standard of integrity."[8] King dreamed of stability, which was "the most essential condition for the permanent prosperity of any business";[9] and he imagined industry spreading throughout the nation until an equilibrium between population and local resources was reached. These hopes for American mining were never fully realized, because the Survey was founded as a bureau of information, not as a reform agency. They do, however, place mineral science in a broader perspective and suggest a social application of the Survey's findings.

While his staff was at work in the Far West, King undertook the dual political task of making the Survey a nationwide operation and increasing its annual budget fivefold. Hewitt's climactic oration of February 1879 had assumed a national scope for the geological bureau; his theme of material riches and scientific knowledge had transcended political boundaries or legal frameworks. He had made the Survey national in vision and name, and now King wanted to make it national in law and fact. To do this he estimated would require half a million dollars annually.

The popular support for King's plans originated in the South, where many people saw industrialization as the means of rebuilding the economy. G. C. Little, the state geologist of Georgia, wrote King that his acquaintance with public opinion from North Carolina to Texas convinced him that work by the Survey would be welcomed.[10] Representative Benjamin

8 S. F. Emmons to H. A. W. Tabor, February 17, 1881, U. S. Geological Survey, Emmons Copybook, Letters Sent, 1879-1886, U. S. National Archives.

9 King, "Introductory Remarks," in Emmons and Becker, *Precious Metals*, xiii.

10 G. C. Little to Clarence King, February 26, 1880, U. S. Geological Survey, Letters Received, 1880.

Wilson of West Virginia reported that "my people are anxious for the geological survey." In June 1879 J. D. C. Atkins informed the House that Tennessee had large deposits of coal and iron and wanted accurate information about them.[11] Congressman Abram Fulkerson of the same state thought that within a radius of 300 miles of Bristol, Tennessee, could be found "a greater amount and a greater variety of minerals than exist in a like area in any other part of the United States."[12] Fulkerson predicted that these minerals would lie untouched unless the federal government identified their location to the capitalists of the world. Frederick Prime, a European-trained mining geologist and iron manufacturer, warned the South that if it neglected its own resources, a few outside capitalists, who could afford to hire engineers or geologists, would seize the region's riches.[13]

King's main argument was that only a national bureau could provide the needed information. Mineral resources were interstate. Gold, for example, was found in four states and six territories. Industrial processes were delicate and depended upon knowledge of scientists from many localities. Engineers, King wrote, must know how "to protect and control the chemical and metallurgical points which decide the values of ores," because "success or ruin often turn on·a fractional per cent of some fatal ingredient."[14] "An ore from Virginia," he explained, "may be best smelted at Baltimore, when mixed with another from Michigan, by means of a fuel from Pennsylvania

11 U.S., *Congressional Record*, 46th Cong., 1st Sess., June 28, 1879, p. 2421.

12 U.S., *Congressional Record*, 47th Cong., 1st Sess., July 11, 1882, p. 5927.

13 F. A. Prime to J. W. Powell, March 19, 1881, U.S. Geological Survey, Letters Received, 1881.

This southern pressure continued even after the nationalization of the Survey. H. G. Davis and J. N. Camden to J. W. Powell, January 5, 1883, J. E. Kenna and J. N. Camden to J. W. Powell, July 26, 1883, L. Q. C. Lamar to J. W. Powell, June 16, 1884, H. G. Davis to J. W. Powell, November 13, 1886, *ibid.*, 1883, 1884, 1886.

14 Clarence King to H. G. Davis, December 15, 1879, U.S. Geological Survey, Letters Sent, 1879.

and a flux from Maryland."[15] A mine owner, faced by some
practical difficulty in the treatment of raw metal, could not
benefit from the experience of others unless he studied for
months or years. Shaky statistics were another technical handicap. In the mining industry no one knew with accuracy the
amounts and valuations of national production. When politicians and economists struggled with the problems of taxa-
tion and tariff, they could only guess the nation's wealth.

For two years King fought unsuccessfully to extend his
bureau's work east of the Mississippi. Probably he was not
surprised when his claim that the Survey already was a national body conflicted with legal opinion in the Department
of the Interior. King cited the Act of 1879, which defined the
Survey's place of business as the "national domain." He maintained that these words meant the entire United States. But
the department ruled that "national domain" confined the
Survey to territories and states with public lands. After an
initial step in June 1879 when the House voted an amendment by Atkins authorizing the director to extend the Survey
to the East, nothing further happened. In the Senate, Davis
of West Virginia and other friends of the Atkins amendment
could not force a vote, although they started discussion in
May 1880. A concurrent attempt in the House to increase
the appropriation was defeated.

The opposition to extension came from those who believed
that public scientific studies were primarily a responsibility of
the states and that federal growth would undermine the state
power, or that economy in government science was important.
A leading opponent was James D. Dana, professor at Yale,
who made a strong statement in the *American Journal of
Science* for December 1879. According to Dana, the Constitution ordered the states to make geological surveys for the
discovery of natural resources. The proposed "infringement
on State rights and assumption of State responsibilities" was
"politically wrong," he continued; the government should

[15] U.S.G.S. *First Annual Report,* 77.

not establish "a Mining Bureau for the country at large."[16]

Dana also dispatched strong letters to several senators. King then solicited support from a number of past and present state geologists. These officials favored his plans, saying that none of the states had done well enough to merit a monopoly of geological study within their boundaries.[17] J. S. Newberry's reply was typical. State research was "an interrupted and irregular patchwork." In many instances local geology had been studied carefully, but since few of the geologists carried their observations over "any great breadth of territory," their generalizations were "entirely incompatible." Newberry also attacked state legislatures, something King dared not do. Some of these sovereign bodies had never authorized surveys. If undertaken, almost all such surveys had been by "political administration or personal jealousies" brought to "premature and more or less abortive conclusion."[18]

Those who advocated the rights of the states in Congress sided with Dana, but having no great popular support and isolated from any professional or economic interest, their opposition was not taken seriously by the leading politicians. In the House J. H. Reagan of Texas held that a federal law creating a geological or scientific survey "would execute no

[16] *American Journal of Science and Arts,* Third Series, XVIII (1879), 496.

[17] T. C. Chamberlin, Wisconsin, J. B. Killebrew, Commissioner of Mines, Tennessee, to Clarence King, February 26, 1880, John Collett, Indiana, James Hall, New York, E. W. Hilgard, California, J. H. Leslie, Pennsylvania, N. S. Shaler, Kentucky, E. A. Smith, Alabama, to Clarence King, February 27, 1880, C. H. Hitchcock, New Hampshire, to Clarence King, February 28, 1880, J. S. Newberry, Ohio, N. H. Winchell, Minnesota, G. H. Cook, New Jersey, March 1, 1880, U. S. Geological Survey, Letters Received, 1880. Only G. H. Cook of New Jersey disliked the centralizing tendency.

[18] J. S. Newberry to Clarence King, March 1, 1880, *ibid.*

"We Texans have to blush," wrote George Stolley, a scientist, "if we can yet—as to the wretched state in which the geology of our broad and beautiful domain remains today. . . . Thousands upon thousands have been squandered . . . but what is the final result:—a pile of ashes, where the old capitol . . . stood, and no other records all the world over—as far attributable to the *state*—of the geology and paleontology of Texas." George Stolley to J. W. Powell, October 29, 1882, *ibid.,* 1882.

provision of the Constitution, either expressed or implied."
And he shuddered at "one of the advanced positions of the
time" that a federal officer executing a federal law need not
respect any state law. But J. G. Cannon of Illinois assured
him that the United States had neither the power nor the
disposition to interfere directly or indirectly with any state
survey. Atkins thought Reagan was "straining the point considerably when he introduces the question of State rights into
a matter of this sort." And G. C. Hazelton of Wisconsin could
not hide his irritation at an amendment requiring a state's
consent to Survey operations within its borders. This amendment, Hazelton said, was "entirely frivolous" and "no one
but an insane person would offer it." Senator Roscoe Conkling
of New York mocked the opposition to a national survey as
the "offended shade of State rights," that "faded sentimen-
tality of the democratic party," causing Senator W. W. Eaton
of Connecticut to accuse him of advocating a "great imperial
policy." Eaton insisted that "the principle of State rights is
a living principle yet, and not a shadow of a shade . . . it is
not one of the old things the democracy talked and dreamed
about fifty years ago, but it has life now."[19]

It was the plea for money that turned the political tide
against King in 1879 and 1880. Dana struck heavily on the retrenchment purpose of the founding. King's plan, he wrote,
was "wholly foreign" to the opinions and objectives of the
committee of the academy, which had aimed at economy,
while the "new scheme . . . would involve millions of outlay
. . . for the strictly geological part and indefinite millions
besides for the economical branch."[20] Important members of
Congress, who might not be moved by the appeal to states'
rights, did listen to the call for economy. The Survey was new

[19] U. S., *Congressional Record*, 46th Cong., 1st Sess., June 28, 1879, pp.
2421-23. Reagan was willing to tolerate the Coast and Geodetic Survey in
the states, because the Constitution authorized federal regulation of
commerce among the states and with foreign countries.
[20] *American Journal of Science and Arts*, Third Series, XVIII (1879),
495.

and no one had yet any results to go by. J. C. S. Blackburn
of Kentucky called a budgetary increase at this time (1880)
"unjudicious," "unwise," "reckless," and "hazardous."[21]

King as a director also seemed to inspire congressional
hostility toward a national Survey. No complaint can be issued against him for lack of energy and purpose in the spring
of 1880. Representative J. H. Blount of Georgia declared that
"gentlemen connected with the survey, who are paid out of
the public treasury, have for months, day after day, lobbied
from one wing of this Capitol to the other to get an increase
of this appropriation."[22] But the Senate, where King had
always been strong, turned against him—particularly Dawes
of Massachusetts, Newton Booth of California, and J. B. Beck
of Kentucky. In June 1880 Booth and Beck prevented a vote
to give King new powers. Beck even persuaded Representative Blount to join the opposition. Beck's statements about
King were "of such a nature & so positive as to compel Blount
. . . to take the course he did."[23] When Becker came to
Washington to receive his Comstock assignment, he found
the director tired and discouraged.

The factors behind the Senate's loss of confidence are not
clear. However, King gave his resignation in March 1881 to
James A. Garfield, the new President, after making sure that
J. W. Powell, in whom King had great confidence, would be
his successor.[24] King said that he resigned because he felt
administration of the Survey left him no time for personal
geological labors, and he also felt he could be more useful
to science as an investigator than as an executive.[25] Actually,
King wanted to enjoy life (which he did for several years in

21 U. S., *Congressional Record*, 46th Cong., 2nd Sess., May 28, 1880,
p. 3926.

22 *Ibid.*, 3924.

23 G. C. Little to J. W. Powell, January 17, 1883, U. S. Geological Survey,
Letters Received, 1883, No. 743.

24 M. H. Adams to R. W. Hooper, March 27, 1881, *The Letters of Mrs.
Henry Adams, 1865-1883*, ed. Ward Thoron (Boston, 1936), 278.

25 Clarence King to the President of the United States, March 11, 1881,
U.S.G.S. *Second Annual Report, 1880-1881* (Washington, 1882), xi.

Europe) and to make a fortune in Mexico (at which he failed).

A judgment of King's accomplishments as director of the Geological Survey must rest on an unfinished performance. He had made a good start in the West. Obeying Congress, he organized a bureau emphasizing the mining interests. He made a good selection of scientists from the older surveys, inspiring some of his staff with such loyalty that they believed the Survey would fail if he resigned.[26] And he launched an ambitious research program. Actual accomplishments, however, were meager: a manuscript topographical map of Eureka, Nevada; and his manifesto for nationalization, the *First Annual Report of the U. S. Geological Survey,* which he paid for out of his own pocket. None of the volumes of research had appeared, though publication of all had been promised by spring of 1881. King's influence, however, lasted beyond his tenure as director. The second director, Powell, immediately sought entry into the eastern states, using King's arguments and strategy. Also, the mining interest remained an important feature of the Survey. But no one was ever to see the bureau as the first director had planned it, for Powell abandoned the idea of multiple studies in mining centers and the development of theories of ore formation.

The record of King's accomplishment as director of the Geological Survey should be compared to the memorable portrait of him in *The Education of Henry Adams.* In his autobiography, Adams eulogized King, who was a close friend. "None of his contemporaries," wrote Adams, "had done so much single-handed, or were likely to leave so deep a trail"; and "he knew America, especially west of the hundredth meridian, better than anyone." Of course King knew a lot about the West and left a deep trail. But this view of King's superiority over his contemporaries cannot be con-

---

[26] G. F. Becker to S. C. T. Becker, December 3, 1879, Arnold Hague to G. F. Becker, November 18, 1880, S. F. Emmons to G. F. Becker, May 1, 1881, George F. Becker Papers, Library of Congress.

firmed from the history of the Geological Survey. Adams also wrote that King was the "only one who stood out in extraordinary prominence as the type and model of what Adams would have liked to be, and of what the American, as he conceived, should have been and was not."[27] The figure which emerges from government documents and private letters is far from ideal. His most unpleasant trait, a cynical and unnecessary deceit, has been exposed more than once—the pretenses during the diamond adventure, the resignation simulated as devotion to science, and his conduct in a brush with the Survey West of the One Hundredth Meridian, which the engineers were holding together in the vain hope that Congress would change its mind. In the summer of 1879, J. D. McChesney, a clerk of Wheeler's, agreed at an unspecified time to join the new Survey. Director King immediately wrote to Stevenson of New York University about his newly won "treasure." He had "hooked" McChesney and "will, one day, land him safely in the Geological Survey basket." He was jocular about this raid on Wheeler's organization: "the tenth commandment says nothing about coveting thy neighbor's clerk." Now the famed wit was in full play: "there are some geologists of the various surveys whom I do not desire, fearing to covet my neighbor's ass." Naturally Wheeler was "wrathy," and King proposed pacifying him with "a letter of distinguished smoothness."[28] Despite King's vanity and hypocrisy, he deserves, more than anyone else, to be called founder of the U. S. Geological Survey, if only because his idea of a survey and his person constituted the Survey in March 1879.

In the next session of Congress Powell exploited southern sentiment to gain admittance to the older states and to double the appropriation to the Survey. On July 11, 1882, Represen-

27 *The Education of Henry Adams: An Autobiography* (Boston, 1918), 308, 309, 311-12.
28 Clarence King to J. J. Stevenson, September 13, 1879, James D. Hague Papers, U. S. Geological Survey Letter Book, 1879-1882, Huntington Library. Clarence King to G. M. Wheeler, *ibid.*

tative Atkins gained House approval for a budgetary increase of $100,000 in the Sundry Civil Appropriation Bill. Another authorization, drafted by Powell himself, "to continue the preparation of a geological map of the United States," was rejected. Without a murmur, Atkins agreed to a motion from the floor that the words "national domain" be substituted for "United States." The director now had more money to spend, but he was still hampered by the ambiguous words "national domain."[29]

In the Senate, support from the Appalachian South was decisive in extending the Survey's scope and budget. Two citizens of nearby states, Jed Hotchkiss of Virginia and J. R. Procter of Kentucky, particularly aided Powell.

Hotchkiss, an expert on Virginia Civil War maps, enlisted the aid of S. N. Yost, editor of the *Valley Virginian*, in persuading Senators William Mahone of Virginia and J. D. Cameron of Pennsylvania to support Powell's request for an expanded survey. Procter, state geologist of Kentucky, was successful in getting help for Powell and the Survey from Kentucky's congressional delegation, which had been hostile to the Survey under Clarence King.[30]

Senator Davis of West Virginia finished the job which Atkins had begun. On August 2, representing the committee on appropriations, he reported the House budget increase in the Sundry Civil Bill. Again the Atkins clause read as originally: "to continue the preparation of a geological map of the United States." Davis also proposed authorization for statistical and metallurgical studies on a national scale: "ten thousand dollars of the amount appropriated . . . may be

[29] U. S., *Congressional Record*, 47th Cong., 1st Sess., July 11, 1882, pp. 5923-30.

[30] Jed Hotchkiss to J. W. Powell, July 10, 15, 1882, U. S. Geological Survey, Letters Received, 1882, No. 893.

Jed Hotchkiss to J. W. Powell, July 5, 1882, to John Paul, to William Mahone, July 15, 1882, to W. C. Kerr, September 4, 1882, Jed Hotchkiss Letter Books, Library of Congress.

applied . . . to the procuring of statistics in relation to mines and mining other than gold and silver and in making chemical analyses of iron, coal, and oil."[31] Consent by the Senate was a formality.[32]

On August 4, there was a reversal of the situation as it had stood when Congress initially established the Survey. A House member, Frank Hiscock of New York, charged the Senate with unfair procedure. The Senate and House had agreed, he said, not to use appropriation bills for original legislation. But other members, impatient of a delay during the last days of a session, shouted, "vote," "vote."[33] The changes by Davis passed easily. On August 8, 1882, President Chester Arthur signed the Sundry Civil Appropriation Bill, and in power as well as in name the scientific bureau became the United States Geological Survey.

Endowed with permanent national status and a rising budget, the Survey was free to organize a research program similar in broad objectives and spirit to the western work before 1879. Also, there were brighter prospects for a diversified Survey than in the days when King, Hayden, and Powell conducted separate explorations. Now that the Survey could enter other regions of the country, it no longer needed to be identified exclusively with the West and the passing frontier. Permanent acceptance by the government and by the American people became a feasible goal.

31 U. S., *Congressional Record,* 47th Cong., 1st Sess., August 2, 1882, p. 6768.
32 For this fundamental legislation, see U. S., *Statutes at Large,* XXII (Washington, 1881-1883), 329.
33 U. S., *Congressional Record,* 47th Cong., 1st Sess., August 4, 1882, p. 6906.

Chapter Four

RESEARCH IN GEOLOGY AND PALEONTOLOGY

In the sciences of geology and paleontology the national Survey accumulated knowledge on an impressive scale and encouraged a fruitful interplay between this knowledge and scientific theory. Powell hired experienced and even famous researchers, made them heads of divisions, and gave them substantial freedom in their intellectual quests. Of course one of these divisions was in physical geology so that American momentum in this field could be maintained. A unit in glacial geology was staffed by scientists from Wisconsin, who had wanted a national survey so that they could study the effects of glaciation on a broad geographical front. A division for New England was organized to examine some complicated strata in western Massachusetts. Powell seemed determined to make the Survey the world's center for paleontology study; he established a number of divisions—one in vertebrate paleontology, several for invertebrate paleontology, and one each in paleobotany and fossil insects. The topic which stimulated the most theorizing among Survey scientists was the rate of change on the earth's surface during geological time. Pressed to answer whether physical change was gradual or sudden, these scientists replied that their research harmonized with the theory that change was gradual. They also speculated on the nature of the scientific fact and the relationship of fact to theory in their methodology.

The same brilliance in the study of land forms, which had made Powell's territorial organization famous, carried over

into the work of the Geological Survey. G. K. Gilbert undertook the study of the bed of a huge ancient lake which he
named Bonneville after the army explorer. Of this great body
of water which had once covered almost all of northern Utah
only Great Salt Lake remains. By reading the present-day
topography Gilbert inferred the physiographic events since
the Pleistocene era. He defined two formative influences: the
land was "sculptured by the beating of rain and by the flow
of rills, and creeks, and rivers," and it also was "sculptured
by the sway of waves and currents." Or, as he expressed it,
"all the hills and mountains above the shore line of Lake
Bonneville bear witness of the play of subaerial agents, while
below that line the slopes betray their subaqueous shaping.
There is a trenchant line between them, and their peculiari-
ties are beautifully contrasted."[1]

Gilbert scored a striking success in defining the stages of
the history of Bonneville. He distinguished five successive
epochs. After a long dry period the first lake was formed,
which although extensive, remained saline because it had no
outlet. Another arid period followed, and the lake disappeared. The second lacustrine epoch occurred when the water
reached the Bonneville shore line, 90 feet above the high level
of the first humid interval. The terrace created by the Bonneville shore line is an obvious part of Utah's topography.
Within this far-flung terrace Lake Bonneville covered 20,000
square miles, an area twice as large as either Lake Erie or
Lake Ontario. Gilbert calculated that the Mormon temple
would then have stood in 850 feet of water. At its highest
stage the lake drained into the basin of the Columbia River,
through an outlet channel that cut rapidly through weak rock
until it met a more resistant material. After the water level
had been lowered about 300 feet, the outflow practically
ceased, and for a long time in the second humid period the

[1] G. K. Gilbert to Clarence King, October 1, 1880, U.S.G.S. *First Annual
Report,* 24.

level was stabilized at its Provo shore line. Finally, the fifth and present dry period reduced the lake to its petty dimensions of historic time.

Since Bonneville was a recent event, Gilbert attempted to relate it to the Ice Age, which also is recent in geological history. His task was difficult, because glacial and lacustrine deposits rarely are found together in the Bonneville basin. Nevertheless, he concluded after long reasoning that the second arid epoch coincided with an interglacial period. He also reported that the bed of the lake warped upward after the weight of the water had been removed and that this rise was accompanied by faulting at the base of the Wasatch Range.[2]

Geologists do not believe Gilbert's work exhausted possibilities for study in the Bonneville basin.[3] They think systematic mapping of sediments on the lake floor will give them additional knowledge of recent movements of the earth's crust and also will reveal substages in the glacial and interglacial periods, which Gilbert could not elucidate during his limited travels across the lake basin. What impresses geologists today about Gilbert is that he wrote comprehensively about a major topic and said so little that they regard as unsatisfactory even after several generations. His monograph, a classic in geomorphology, is a supreme achievement of the nineteenth-century Survey.

The other important scientist in the field of physical geol-

2 G. K. Gilbert, *Lake Bonneville* (Washington, 1890), Chapters III, VI, VII.

Gilbert's masterpiece inspired I. C. Russell to write the history of Lake Lahontan in northwestern Nevada. Lakes Winnemucca, Walker, and Carson are located in the bed of this ancient body of water. Like Bonneville, Lahontan passed through two humid epochs, separated by a period of desiccation. Russell also believed that this arid period coincided with an interglacial phase. I. C. Russell, *Geological History of Lake Lahontan, a Quaternary Lake of Northwestern Nevada* (Washington, 1885).

3 C. H. Hunt, H. D. Varnes, and H. E. Thomas, *Lake Bonneville: Geology of Northern Utah Valley, Utah,* Geological Survey Professional Paper No. 257-A (Washington, 1953), 2, 4, 5, 15, 17, 18, 43.

ogy was Clarence Edmund Dutton, an army captain. Powell had hired him in 1875 without an outlay of salary by asking the Secretary of War to assign Dutton for geological duty. After his first volume on the high plateau region of central Utah, Dutton concentrated on the Grand Canyon district of northwestern Arizona and an adjacent portion of Utah. His *Tertiary History of the Grand Cañon District,* appearing in 1882, was the first monograph published by the U. S. Geological Survey.

Dutton's study focused on the plateaus north of the Colorado River. He stressed the magnitude and decisiveness of erosion in the physical history of the district; the strata of two eras in geological time—the Mesozoic and the Tertiary (Cenozoic) —had been washed away. "Even the mind of the geologist," he wrote, "may falter before accepting a conclusion so portentous."[4] He reasoned correctly that before the deep chasms had been cut the plateau country had been planed down by erosion almost to base level. The present cycle of canyon formation could have begun only when a powerful uplift rejuvenated stream water, an uplift which the author believed to be quite recent.[5] Scenic description and rapture were a major ingredient of Dutton's writing. Adopting an effusive style, he gave picturesque descriptions of the vast panorama, the superlative colors, and the rock forms which resembled human constructs. Contemporaries responded favorably to both the science and the nature writing. Dana found Dutton's report "excellent in all respects."[6] Archibald Geikie of England's Geological Survey concluded his all-round tribute with these words: "The United States may be heartily congratulated."[7]

[4] "The Physical Geology of the Grand Cañon District," U.S.G.S. *Second Annual Report,* 57. C. E. Dutton, *Tertiary History of the Grand Cañon District* (Washington, 1882), 30, 75.

[5] *Tertiary History of the Grand Cañon District,* 99.

[6] J. D. Dana to J. W. Powell, June 9, 1882, U. S. Geological Survey, Letters Received, 1882.

[7] *Nature,* XXVII (1883), 357.

Today, the shortcomings of *Tertiary History* have been identified. In stratigraphy Dutton was overly general, leaving to twentieth-century scientists most of the work of distinguishing, naming, and placing the formations in their exact temporal relations.[8] He thought that the Mesozoic strata originated in the sea and that the Tertiary were deposited in a vast inland lake, whereas geologists now consider that both were largely terrestrial in origin. Nor do today's scientists agree with Dutton's statement that the drainage of the Colorado River antedates present topography. Although *Tertiary History* largely repeats the original thinking of Powell and Gilbert on erosion, Dutton was apparently inspired by his exercise, for he soon introduced a first-rate idea into geomorphology. Scientists already realized that when eroded materials were deposited they sank because of their weight, "just as a railway embankment across a bog sinks into it."[9] Dutton reasoned that if this subsidence of the earth's crust was caused by increased weight, there would be a corresponding uplift where erosion had removed the load. Dutton coined the word "isostasy" to describe this plasticity of the earth's crust, this tendency of rock masses to approach equilibrium. His presentation of this phenomenon established it as a major doctrine of geology.

Expansion eastward allowed Survey scientists to participate in a fascinating discovery made in the nineteenth century—the Ice Age, and its effects. Although decades had elapsed since Louis Agassiz and several other Swiss naturalists advanced the theory that enormous masses of ice once occupied the northern hemisphere, geologists were still marveling at the event and of course studying it. "A continuous sheet of ice," wrote W J

8 H. E. Gregory, *Geology and Geography of the Zion Park Region of Utah and Arizona*, Geological Survey Professional Paper No. 220 (Washington, 1950), 46, 50, 71, 112, 142.

9 C. E. Dutton, "On Some of the Greater Problems of Physical Geology," *Bulletin* of the Philosophical Society of Washington, XI (1892), 54. In this article Dutton introduced the word "isostasy."

McGee, one of the Survey's glaciologists, "hundreds or thousands of feet in thickness and hundreds of thousands of square
miles in extent" crept "sluggishly over hill and valley, lowland
and plateau, even mountain and lake, from a polar source
toward a tropical sun."[10] "The effect of the great ice invasions," Powell said, "was to work over the old surface, mixing
up the soils and subsoils, filing down the prominences, grind-
ing up, in a greater or less degree, loose rock material and
rasping fresh material from the rock surface, and at length
spreading out the whole over the area in a mantle, which
gave not only a new topography but a new basis for the
formation of soils."[11] He and his colleagues appreciated the
effect of the ice masses on flora and fauna, how vegetation
and animal life were altered or destroyed. They considered
astronomy and physics in their search for causes, investigating
the complex motion of the earth as a planet and speculating
about sun conditions which might influence climate. Artifacts
found in the glacial gravels suggested man had established
himself in the New World by the time the ice invasions were
reaching their climax. But these artifacts were scattered and
possibly were deposited by the American Indian. The ensuing
controversy about the age of man in the New World involved
the director and other members of the Survey. Powell thought
that if the early relics of man and the early forms of civilization were related to the glacial period, then the study of the
Ice Age could reveal facts about the origin of mankind. And
the study of man's origin had moral as well as intellectual
consequences.[12]

T. C. Chamberlin, former state geologist in Wisconsin,
organized the glacial division of the Survey. This division
examined terminal moraines—those masses of gravel, boul-

10 W J McGee, "The Pleistocene History of Northeastern Iowa," U.S.G.S.
Eleventh Annual Report (Washington, 1891), 280.
11 "Report of the Director," U.S.G.S. *Fourteenth Annual Report* (Washington, 1893), 113.
12 *Ibid.,* 114.

ders, and earth which mark the limits of important glacial advances. Chamberlin began tracing the moraine which terminated the second glacial epoch; J. E. Todd became an authority on the moraines of the Dakotas; and Frank Leverett investigated the moraines and glacial drift in the Ohio Valley. The three of them, along with W J McGee, who was working in Iowa, made permanent contributions to the knowledge of Ice Age strata.[13]

Progress in the study of terminal moraines went so far that in 1888 R. D. Salisbury of the Survey, while spending the summer in Germany, detected a system of moraines analogous to American forms, "but unlike anything previously discriminated by German geologists."[14] At the same time glacial study proved complex, defying rapid conquest. Starting with the idea of one advance and retreat of the ice sheet in northeastern and north central United States, Chamberlin and others later concluded there had been multiple phenomena: two, three, or even four distinct invasions had occurred. Chamberlin also came to realize that his terminal moraine was not "a simple continuous ridge," or even a number of parallel ridges, but "a broad, irregular range of confusedly heaped drift."[15] There were several kinds of water-laid and ice-laid deposits, and each category must be separated from the product of post-glacial erosion and deposition.

The Survey also conducted studies in western Massachusetts, where Raphael Pumpelly, J. E. Wolff, and T. N. Dale spent three years during the 1880's on the Paleozoic and

13 T. C. Chamberlin, "Preliminary Paper on the Terminal Moraine of the Second Glacial Epoch," U.S.G.S. *Third Annual Report* (Washington, 1883), 295-402. W J McGee, "The Pleistocene History of Northeastern Iowa," U.S.G.S. *Eleventh Annual Report,* 199-577. Frank Leverett, *The Illinois Glacial Lobe* (Washington, 1899).

See also T. C. Chamberlin, "The Rock-Scorings of the Great Ice Invasions," U.S.G.S. *Seventh Annual Report* (Washington, 1888), 155-248.

14 "Report of the Director," U.S.G.S. *Tenth Annual Report* (Washington, 1890), 22.

15 "Preliminary Paper on the Terminal Moraine of the Second Glacial Epoch," U.S.G.S. *Third Annual Report,* 310.

pre-Cambrian strata.[16] Pumpelly concentrated his field force on two prominent topographic features: the Hoosac Range, an extension of the Green Mountains of Vermont into Massachusetts, and Mount Greylock, a spur of the Taconic Mountains that lie along the New York-Massachusetts border and in southwestern Vermont. Wolff gave excellent descriptions of two formations in the Hoosac Range. In stratification, he discovered compelling evidence that the lowermost Paleozoic rock rests unconformably on the pre-Cambrian granite gneiss. Dale demonstrated the folded structure of Mount Greylock, and Pumpelly showed that the schists of Hoosac and Greylock were the same. The areal maps of the geology, which Pumpelly and his associates prepared, presented graphically knowledge which experts have been able to use ever since.[17]

Hoosac or Greylock did not yield easily to geologic study. Stress and heat had altered the rocks so drastically that identifying and dating them could not be completed during one or even several campaigns. Another complicating factor, ignored at the time, was the magnitude of the displacement. Large masses of the distorted strata were overthrusts from the east, which may have moved a considerable distance. The work of Pumpelly, Wolff, and Dale made a respectable start in a region where the geology is still obscure.[18]

In 1887, Pumpelly learned with surprise of some original research in the geology of Massachusetts which, as a complement to his own studies, deserved recognition by the Survey. For 15 years B. K. Emerson of the Amherst College faculty had been conducting extensive studies on both sides of the Connecticut River. After a day's interview with Emerson,

[16] *Geology of the Green Mountains in Massachusetts* (Washington, 1894).

[17] Louis M. Prindle and Eleanora Bliss Knopf, "Geology of the Taconic Quadrangle," *American Journal of Science*, Fifth Series, XXIV (1932), 257, 270, 271, 285, 291, 301.

[18] Chester R. Longwell, *Guidebook I: Excursion A-1, Eastern New York and Western New England*, International Geological Congress, XVI Session, United States, 1933, pp. 87, 90.

Pumpelly praised the extent and quality of the findings, and he urged immediate publication. Emerson's monograph of 800 pages appeared in 1898 as the *Geology of Old Hampshire County, Massachusetts.* It was a voluminous and accurate description of geology and mineralogy that also discussed economic aspects such as the condition and progress of quarries and mines and the use and value of building stone and road materials.

. The Survey gained scientific stature in the summer of 1882 when O. C. Marsh joined the bureau as vertebrate paleontologist. He had only recently made his greatest discovery—the fossil remains of toothed birds—which Yale College expeditions of the 1870's had uncovered in the Niobrara chalk, an upper Cretaceous limestone of western Kansas. *Odontornithes: A Monograph on the Extinct Toothed Birds of North America* had been published in 1880 as the seventh and last volume of the Exploration of the Fortieth Parallel. Powell allotted space in the *Third Annual Report* for recapitulation.[19]

Marsh's second monograph concerned the Dinocerata, largest land mammals of Eocene time. In size and proportion they were intermediate between elephant and rhinoceros, and they had hoofs, but no trunks. Three pair of bony, hornlike protuberances on the skull, and dagger or saberlike teeth were other features of these strange animals, whose fossils Marsh found in an ancient lake basin of western Wyoming. Marsh identified three genera and 23 species. But the permanent value of his research was diminished substantially because of the rivalry with Cope over naming these mammals. Cope had made similar discoveries in the same territory, and the haste of both men to publish in the scientific journals, thus securing the taxonomic right, produced a confusion of terms for twentieth-century paleontologists.[20]

19 "Birds with Teeth," U.S.G.S. *Third Annual Report,* 49-88.
20 Charles Schuchert and C. M. LeVene, *O. C. Marsh: Pioneer in Paleontology* (New Haven, 1940), 471-73, and H. F. Osborn, *Cope: Master Naturalist,* 177-79.

While on the Survey, Marsh pushed ahead with his collection of dinosaurs, digging up dozens of genera and species. His synopsis of these Mesozoic reptiles in the U.S.G.S. *Sixteenth Annual Report* is considered the beginning of modern classification.[21] His restorations on paper made good popular science, and they were copied all over the world.

Invertebrate paleontology was the mainstay of geologists in determining the order and succession of local deposits and in correlating these local deposits with others across the continent. C. D. Walcott organized a Paleozoic division of invertebrate paleontology; C. A. White, who came from Hayden's survey, established a Mesozoic division; and W. H. Dall, formerly with the Coast Survey, directed a Cenozoic division. All three division leaders published correlation papers with White alone submitting half a dozen manuscripts over a three-year period in the mid-1880's.[22]

These scientists also studied specific animal forms. Walcott concentrated on trilobites, marine invertebrates which dominated Cambrian life and were found worldwide and therefore could be used for intercontinental correlation. He also prepared an important monograph on the fossil medusae, which were jellyfish. White and Dall published papers on mollusks. White reviewed the nonmarine fossil mollusca of North Amer-

[21] "The Dinosaurs of North America," U.S.G.S. *Sixteenth Annual Report* (Washington, 1896), 143-414.

[22] C. D. Walcott, *Correlation Papers: Cambrian*, Geological Survey Bulletin No. 81 (Washington, 1891); C. A. White, *Correlation Papers: Cretaceous*, Geological Survey Bulletin No. 82 (Washington, 1891); W. H. Dall and G. D. Harris, *Correlation Papers: Neocene*, Geological Survey Bulletin No. 84 (Washington, 1892).

White's decisions on the boundary between the Mesozoic and the Cenozoic were necessary for contemporary mapmaking, but recent research has shown them to be outdated. C. A. White, *On the Mesozoic and Cenozoic Paleontology of California*, Geological Survey Bulletin No. 15 (Washington, 1885), 13; also, *On the Relation of the Laramie Molluscan Fauna to that of the Succeeding Fresh-Water Eocene and Other Groups*, Geological Survey Bulletin No. 34 (Washington, 1886), 17. For later interpretations of the Chico, Tejon, and Fort Union formations, see Charles Schuchert and C. O. Dunbar, *A Textbook of Geology: Part II: Historical Geology*, 355, 386, 397.

ica, and Dall the Tertiary and Pleistocene mollusks of the southern Atlantic and Gulf coasts.[23]

Paleobotany and fossil insects were two other divisions of the Survey. Lester Frank Ward began cataloguing American fossil plants and adding to the collections. His findings on the cycadeoids, flowering plants of the Mesozoic, opened the way for more definitive research of the twentieth century. S. H. Scudder contributed to the literature of fossil insects with six bulletins, two monographs, and two papers in the annual reports. He found his source materials near Florissant, Colorado, in the ash beds of an extinct Miocene lake. Florissant was the richest locality in the world for fossil insects, excepting only the Baltic amber deposits. Scudder had collected 20,000 specimens by the end of the 1880's.

The argument over the rate of physical change on the earth's surface had been a part of the history of geology for a century. The traditional view, called catastrophism, held that when change came, it was great and violent. As the nineteenth century advanced, however, most American geologists leaned toward uniformitarianism, or the moderation and continuity of physical change. In all his studies Hayden took the position that the West owed "its present configuration" to uniform and slow movements.[24] Powell also was a uniformitarian, finding support for his position in his studies of the Colorado Plateau. Uniformitarianism was inescapable once Powell realized the sculpturing power of rain, stream, and waves. Obviously these

[23] C. A. White, "A Review of the Non-Marine Fossil Mollusca of North America," U.S.G.S. *Third Annual Report*, 411-550. W. H. Dall, *List of Marine Mollusca, Comprising the Quaternary Fossils and Recent Forms from American Localities between Cape Hatteras and Cape Roque, Including the Bermudas*, Geological Survey Bulletin, No. 24 (Washington, 1885). For a twentieth-century appreciation, see C. R. Weaver, "Invertebrate Paleontology and Historical Geology from 1850 to 1950," *A Century of Progress in the Natural Sciences, 1853-1953* (San Francisco, 1955), 710.

[24] *Preliminary Report of the U.S. Geological Survey of Wyoming* (Washington, 1871), 165.

elements worked slowly. Their influence on the present face of western land was scarcely perceptible, yet because of their persistence they accomplished an enormous denudation and transfer of materials in Utah and Arizona.

A provocative speech by Clarence King at the Yale Sheffield Scientific School in 1877 gave new life to the older view. He favored the catastrophism theory, asserting it had factual backing in western geology—the rapid sinking of the ocean bottom during the Paleozoic era, the abrupt mountain building during Mesozoic time when the entire middle of the continent domed up, and the more recent lava and ice flows. He thought religion and the wisdom of the ages also affirmed his view, and he criticized the "British School of Uniformitarianism," founded by Sir Charles Lyell, because it insisted on a single, constant rate for earth dynamics in past, present, and future, admitting no cause for change except such ordinary agencies as rain, snow, ice, and so forth.[25]

Scientists of the Survey, however, unanimously supported uniformitarian theory. Perhaps Gilbert's work was the most telling, for both he and the first director had studied dynamics of mountain building in the Great Basin. In his Bonneville masterpiece he contradicted King on the Wasatch Range, the largest mountain mass in Utah and one example of the Basin Range type of structure.[26] Gilbert contended the Wasatch had recently increased in height and was still growing, illustrating a measured and continuous process.[27]

Bailey Willis, another geologist of the Survey, testified for uniformitarianism in a long paper on "The Mechanics of Appalachian Structure," a field and laboratory study which stressed the rate and magnitude of the Appalachian movement, originating in the contraction or the yield and flow of rock materials. Willis wrote that "the development must have

[25] "Catastrophism and Evolution," *The American Naturalist*, XI (1877), 449-59.
[26] See above, p. 32.
[27] *Lake Bonneville*, 359-60.

been so gradual as scarcely to become effective in geologic ages, and yet the force was of an intensity so pronounced and involved masses so prodigious that it must have become irresistible."[28] N. S. Shaler of Harvard University, who published with the Survey on the geology of the New England coast, wrote in 1891 that "geologists now believe that the continents have grown slowly from the seas, and the mountains with all their exhibitions of titanic energy have likewise gradually come to their present state."[29] Three years later W J McGee, in a paper before the Geological Society of America on "The Extension of Uniformitarianism to Deformation," insisted that gradualism be applied to mass movements (mountains) as well as to particle movements of the earth's crust.[30]

At the same time American geologists did not ignore violent agencies and agreed to a varying rate of change on the earth's surface. They were not uniformitarians in King's sense of the word. Gilbert discussed the extra work that a flooded stream could do because of its increased momentum, and he recognized the role of storms in shaping shore features. I. C. Russell prepared an article on the Pleistocene history of Mono Valley in eastern California, the Pleistocene including the ice epochs and their recessive intervals. Russell emphasized that compared with the present the Pleistocene was on the average "a time of greatly expanded water surface, increased glacial action, and more energetic volcanic activity." He did not regard this conclusion as denying the Survey's fundamental point of view, writing: "Could we look into the future with as much accuracy as we are able to review the past, it would be evident that changes are in progress that in time will equal the appar-

28 "The Mechanics of Appalachian Structure," U.S.G.S. *Thirteenth Annual Report* (Washington, 1892), 281. Years later this paper was still being praised. Joseph Barrell, "A Century of Geology: The Growth of Knowledge of Earth Structure," *American Journal of Science,* Fourth Series, XLVI (1918), 167.

29 *Nature and Man in America* (New York, 1891), 131-32.

30 "The Extension of Uniformitarianism to Deformation," *Bulletin* of the Geological Society of America, VI (1894), 55-70.

ent revolutions which occurred during the Quaternary [Pleistocene]. This, as everyone will see, is but a restatement of the uniformitarian belief of geologists."[31]

The philosophers of the Survey gave a historical dimension to the issue, which was lacking in King's presentation. No one wanted the return of an attitude which had prevailed before Lyell. Paleontologist White denied that universal extinction of species had ever occurred. Dutton, preparing for volcanic studies, visited the Hawaiian Islands and saw the huge crater of Mokuaweoweo. "Fifty or sixty years ago," he observed, "most geologists would at once have conjectured that it was blown out by some stupendous explosion . . . . Such an explanation would be wholly unsatisfactory to the geologist of the present day. Cataclysms are not postulated in modern geological science without evidence amounting to positive proof."[32] McGee considered the period before Lyell as prescientific. "It is vain," he cried, "to explain the seen in terms of the unseen; and the time is gone by for the primitive appeal to the rare and remote in explanation for the common and near at hand."[33]

But there was a feeling in scientific circles toward the end of the nineteenth century that the immediate successors of Lyell had been so determined to avoid the miraculous and mysterious in nature that they became oversuspicious of the abnormal or violent. The discovery of the Ice Age (an unnatural and revolutionary force) shook the belief in a quiet and gentle nature. McGee was epigrammatic about the discovery: "to the radical uniformitarian whose opinions were tinctured by antagonism to an injurious but decadent catastrophism, it [the Ice Age] was an unsavory resurrection." And he commended the "moderate cataclysm with which the modern ge-

[31] "Quaternary History of Mono Valley, California," U.S.G.S. *Eighth Annual Report* (Washington, 1889), 390-91.
[32] "Hawaiian Volcanoes," U.S.G.S. *Fourth Annual Report* (Washington, 1884), 142.
[33] "The Extension of Uniformitarianism to Deformation," 70.

ologist is content—the swallowing up of islands, the sudden encroachment of the sea, or the shattering of rocks by earth-quakes."[34] The fallacy of King's Sheffield address was its one-sided presentation when actually he knew better. He slipped in a sentence which undermined his whole argument: "With our present light, geological history seems to be a dovetailing together of the two ideas."[35]

Survey geologists regarded uniformitarian theory as indispensable to the integrity of science. Ordinarily they could not observe directly the phenomena they studied. Therefore, they had to deduce these bygone causes and processes. Catastrophism, by introducing the unexpected, stood as a barrier to fruitful deduction. Only by assuming that nature acts consistently could geologists advance with certainty into the past and unknown history. Geology would cease to exist as a science if they doubted the temporal regularity of physical events. This unbroken continuity of physical processes in past, present, and future McGee called *"The Uniformity of Nature,"* borrowing "Huxley's happy phrase." It was "a (if not *the*) cardinal principle of science," and "must be credited largely to Geology."[36]

Assuming uniformitarianism, geologists were able to understand and organize large numbers of facts. They, and not the catastrophists, brought law and order to earth history.[37] In

[34] "The Pleistocene History of Northeastern Iowa," U.S.G.S. *Eleventh Annual Report,* 280-90.

[35] "Catastrophism and Evolution," 463.

[36] "Cardinal Principles of Science," *Proceedings* of the Washington Academy of Sciences, II (1900), 6.

[37] When Henry Adams reviewed his friend's Sheffield address for *The Nation,* he said that King had not yet suggested "any theory as to the law or laws which may govern these recurring phenomena [catastrophes], without which he will have simply succeeded in depriving us of Lyell's system without offering us a system of his own." *The Nation,* XXV (1877), 137. *The Nation: Index of Contributors, 1865-1917* (New York, 1953), 2.

In *The Education* (p. 313), years later, Adams wrote differently. "The young men of the Fortieth Parallel [Exploration] had Californian instincts; they were brothers of Bret Harte. They felt no leanings toward the simple uniformities of Lyell and Darwin; they saw little proof of slight and imperceptible changes; to them, catastrophe was the law of

their minds uniformitarian theory and the development of geological knowledge merged into a unified picture of nature.

Most of the other commentary on methodology by geologists revolved around the two procedures of fact finding and theorizing. Gilbert offered a definition of a scientific fact or observation. First, he said, it endeavored "to discriminate the phenomena observed from the observer's inference in regard to them, and to record the phenomena pure and simple." He knew that ordinarily the observer did not grasp the "untainted" fact, because "perception and inference are so intimately associated that a body of inference has become incorporated in the constitution of the mind"; and language, "the creator and imitator of the mind," stood between the investigator and the pure fact. Insofar as the observer tried to overcome these innate or social biases, his effort tended to be scientific and distinctive. Secondly, the scientific investigator was not indiscriminate in collecting facts; he concentrated upon a limited number, and this practice sharpened his view as compared with that of the ordinary observer.[38]

In the district of the Grand Canyon, Dutton said that explaining and unifying the facts he found was "like trying to restore the newly discovered fragments of an antique vase which had been scattered and a portion of them recovered. Each fragment by itself is of minor importance and gives no definite idea of the shape and size of the vase. But when a number of them have been matched and the broken edges are seen to join, even though considerable portion be want-

change; they cared little for simplicity and much for complexity." If Adams really believed that geological thought had not advanced beyond Lyell and Darwin, he was antiquated. And he wrote unfairly in marrying uniformitarianism to simplicity. Geologists in the Survey found complexity everywhere in their science, yet they were overwhelmingly uniformitarian in outlook.

[38] "The Inculcation of Scientific Method by Example," *American Journal of Science,* Third Series, XXXI (1886), 284-85.

ing, we may still perceive the original design and compute its dimensions."[39] He emphatically rejected one kind of unification of the facts, which his metaphor might have suggested: "The rivers of the Atlantic States, from the Hudson southward, cut through the Appalachian ridges by narrow gorges, or gaps, which seem to have been quarried out for the purpose. Geology, however, does not take account of 'purpose' or 'design,' but seeks its explanations in 'natural' causes alone. It asks by what natural processes were these gorges made?"[40] Gilbert filled in the specific features of this causation, proposing that phenomena in nature were arranged in chains with each link in the chain the necessary consequent of the preceding one and the necessary antecedent of the following one. The rising sun was consequent on the rotation of the earth and "the logical antecedent" of morning light. He explained that every link had more than one consequence; the rising of the sun depended on the position of the earth's axis as well as on its rotation, and it produced morning heat as well as morning light. "Antecedent and consequent relations are therefore not merely linear, but constitute a plexus; and this plexus pervades nature," he said. It was the province of research, Gilbert concluded, to discover the simple and complex antecedents of phenomena; these were the "deeper relations which constitute the order of nature."[41]

When the fact finding and theorizing were properly related by Survey geologists, the conquest of knowledge was assured. Arnold Hague analyzed geyser waters in Yellowstone Park and found them to contain arsenic and sulphureted hydrogen in varying quantities. From these facts he inferred that sulphide of arsenic must be deposited under favorable conditions in vents and chambers of hot springs and solfataras. After long seeking he found two such sulphides in Norris Basin within

39 C. E. Dutton to J. W. Powell, October 3, 1881, U.S.G.S. Second Annual Report, 9.
40 "Physical Geology of the Grand Cañon District," ibid., 60-61.
41 "The Inculcation of Scientific Method by Example," 285-86.

the park, and Powell drew the moral for his annual report in 1889. Hague's experience was "an interesting demonstration of the excellence of the methods pursued in the Yellowstone National Park Division, and indeed of the certainty of scientific reasoning in general."[42] A new division of geology, Powell said in 1893, had been founded on the reciprocity of fact and theory. Formerly the glacial mantle of boulder-bearing clay, gravel, loam, and sand was called diluvium or drift—believed to be the product of some primordial flood. Meanwhile, observers accumulated a great many facts about the drift which were not consistent with the idea of a general deluge. This lack of rapport ended when Louis Agassiz rejected the standing theory and reinterpreted the facts under the glacial hypothesis. Then progress in glacial geology could begin.

The abuse of the scientific method lay in making either fact or theory an end in itself. Both Powell and Chamberlin thought there had been too much isolated fact finding in the post-Civil War period, burdening the literature with trivia and threatening the field with loss of vitality.[43] Dutton reminded his readers that the fact gathering should lead into the theorizing or interpretive stage. "The geologist," he wrote, "seeks for facts in order to learn geological history and causation—in short evolution. He picks up his facts much as the vagabond prospector picks up float ore or pans for a few colors in every gulch and when he finds them seeks to trace them back to their sources, dreaming always of bonanzas."[44] Gilbert said that the method of hypothesis was the method of science. But he also warned against the investigator who, having transcended the facts, no longer gave them their proper weight. Although theory was the higher goal, it remained subject to

[42] "Report of the Director," U.S.G.S. *Tenth Annual Report*, 24.
[43] T. C. Chamberlin, "The Method of Multiple Working Hypotheses," *Science*, XV (1890), 93; J. W. Powell, "Biographical Notice of Archibald Robertson Marvine," *Bulletin* of the Philosophical Society of Washington, II (1874-1876), Appendix X, vi.
[44] C. E. Dutton to J. W. Powell, October 3, 1881, U.S.G.S. *Second Annual Report*, 8.

the limitations of imperfect observation. A new dissonant fact could unsettle the grandest, the most useful, and the most widely accepted hypothesis. "In the domain of the world's knowledge there is no infallibility," he said.[45]

The Survey singled out G. F. Wright, Congregationalist minister and professor at Oberlin, as the best example of excessive attachment to theory. Wright, a vigorous and constructive glaciologist, advocated a unitary view of the Ice Age— that there had been only one advance and retreat of the ice sheet. This unitary view was accepted doctrine in Civil War times until extensive research by Chamberlin and others disproved it. Nevertheless, Wright held firmly to the older opinion.[46]

Some Survey geologists suggested that controversy, which would lead to survival of the fittest, would eliminate the dogmatic hypothesis. Chamberlin's proposal was more practical, recognizing as it did the dynamic nature of geology. He urged scientists to embrace every tenable hypothesis concerning natural events. "The analytic process," he said, "the development and demonstration of criteria, and the sharpening of discrimination, receive powerful impulse from the co-ordinate working of several hypotheses." The scholar acquired the "habit of parallel or complex thought";[47] a number of causes were necessary, for example, to explain the origin of the Great Lakes. By reshaping its method the geological profession could keep abreast of the growing complexity of earth science and continue the advancement of learning.

[45] "The Origin of Hypotheses," *Science*, New Series, III (1896), 12.
[46] See, for example, G. F. Wright, *The Glacial Boundary in Western Pennsylvania, Ohio, Kentucky, Indiana, and Illinois* (with an introduction by T. C. Chamberlin), Geological Survey Bulletin No. 58 (Washington, 1890).
[47] "The Method of Multiple Working Hypotheses," *Science*, XV (1890), 93-94.

Chapter Five

ADVANCEMENT IN TOPOGRAPHY:
THE NATIONAL MAP

The project of a national topographic map was the most surprising consequence of Survey expansion in 1882, becoming dominant in the bureau's activity for a decade. An objective of both the War and Interior Departments during the 1870's had been an atlas for the western possessions of the United States. When the Survey began in 1879, however, topography declined as a government science, as Congress refused to make it a major component of a federal bureau. Director King accepted this decision, and in all the discussion about a national survey between 1879 and 1882 topographical science was virtually ignored. The minds of lawmakers were fixed upon southern regions, their economic exploitation, and the contribution geology could make to this. The scientists were interested in geological studies which they could initiate under government auspices. Yet immediately after congressional consent for the Survey to move eastward in 1882, a topographical or geographical division was established. Within 12 years this division entered every state and territory and mapped 600,000 square miles—20 percent of the nation. Director Powell was responsible for this rapid development, which he did not report to Congress. He made the national map a personal quest, intending to complete it in 20 or 30 years. Originally Powell had valued topography in scientific surveys because it made the best foundation for geological mapping. In Utah he decided that a digest of physical features would help agrarian pioneers locate themselves to best advantage. In 1884 he gave the highest priority to topographical mapping, telling a congressional commission that "a Government cannot do any scientific work of more value to the people at large."[1]

To begin his large and bold enterprise Powell organized a corps of topographers. He needed 50 men immediately, more than the original staff of the Survey, and six years later he would employ 100 field workers. Recruiting was based on the experience, education, or political influence of the candidate.[2] Henry Gannett, the chief of the division of geography since April 1882, had spent seven years with Hayden. The director introduced two assistants from his old survey, A. H. Thompson and J. H. Renshawe. Another worker from the West was R. U. Goode, who had worked first with Wheeler and then with the Northern Transcontinental Survey, the ephemeral project of a private railroad. Gilbert Thompson transferred from the Corps of Army Engineers, where he had mapped the Civil War battlefields of Virginia and Maryland. Marcus Baker had served previously with the Coast and Geodetic Survey. Professor Trowbridge of the Columbia School of Mines recommended several of the school's graduates, including E. M. Douglas and H. M. Wilson, who had reconnoitered for a Mexican railroad. The two became stalwarts of the topographic division. Another person with railroad experience who joined the Survey was G. T. Hawkins, a civil engineer from Mississippi. Since unskilled labor could be used in the field, employment there was subject to political preference, and most topographical parties in the 1880's had at least one relative or favorite of a senator or representative. When state geologist Procter of Kentucky submitted the names of six candidates, Powell hired four of them. Many of these political appointees turned into loyal and qualified public servants. Perhaps the

[1] U. S., Senate Misc. Doc. No. 82, 49th Cong., 1st Sess., 40.

[2] For this paragraph see Henry Gannett to Clarence King, June 10, 1879, to J. W. Powell, April 15, 1882, Gilbert Thompson to J. W. Powell, March 29, 1882, U. S. Geological Survey, Letters Received, 1879, 1882.

best example was A. P. Davis, who enlisted in August 1882
after Powell had telegraphed John Davis of Kansas, a brother-
in-law and ex-congressman, that he should send his boy to
grow up in the Survey.[3] Davis began as a barometer reader in
the southern Appalachians and later became director of the
Reclamation Service.

Because of the hurry about the national map topographers
borrowed generously by compilation from past mapping, assuming the merit and the usefulness of the work under Hayden, King, and Powell. One hundred thousand square miles of
Wheeler's maps proved acceptable. From maps of the General
Land Office topographers lifted the drainage detail and placed
it within a network of independently determined latitudes,
longitudes, and altitudes. Coast and Geodetic Survey triangulation also saved time and money. Gannett searched county
maps of the Blue Ridge and the Shenandoah Valley, compiled
originally by Jackson's Army of the Valley. He judged the
"Meigs" map of West Virginia, drawn up by Lieutenant J. R.
Meigs on Civil War battlefields and countryside, to be "excellent."[4] Railroad maps, which gave altitudes, were also used,
although these were often untrustworthy. Powell expressed
confidence, however, that with care and modest field work the
larger part of these computations could be salvaged. In the
past, he said, Gannett had obtained good results from similar
sources west of the Mississippi.[5]

Powell proceeded with constructing the national map as the
opportunity presented itself. He designated the first broad
front as the Appalachian country south of the Mason and

[3] J. W. Powell to John Davis, August 14, 1882, U. S. Geological Survey,
Letters Sent, 1882. See also J. R. Procter to J. W. Powell, June 4, 1883,
ibid., Letters Received, 1883.
[4] Henry Gannett to J. W. Powell, May 2, 1883, U. S. Geological Survey,
Letters Received, 1883.
[5] J. W. Powell to the Secretary of the American Metrological Society,
January 30, 1883; J. W. Powell to the Chief of Engineers, Southern Pacific
Railroad, May 5, 1882, U. S. Geological Survey, Letters Sent, 1883, 1882.
"Report of the Director," U.S.G.S. *Fourth Annual Report,* xix-xx.

Taken from U.S.G.S. Fourth Annual Report, Plate 1

0   50   100   150   200 MILES

AREA OF TOPOGRAPHIC MAPPING IN THE SOUTH

Dixon line, preparing for the geological studies pledged there
as the condition of Survey expansion eastward. In the summer
of 1882, Gannett began mapping in an isolated region where
five states lay close together—Virginia, North Carolina, West
Virginia, Kentucky, and Tennessee. From Bristol in southwest
Virginia, the chief geographer sent three parties into the forest.
One led by F. M. Pearson moved directly west along the
Virginia-Tennessee boundary to the Cumberland Gap, the
great passageway for early pioneers. Then Pearson turned and
worked northeastward up the Virginia-Kentucky border to
Pine Mountain. The other two parties journeyed to Roan
High Knob in western North Carolina before beginning oper-
ations. Then Morris Bien moved northeastward, partly in
Tennessee and partly in North Carolina, with the main section of his territory lying on the headwaters of the Kanawha
and New Rivers. The second party, led by C. M. Yeates,
headed in a southwest direction from Roan High Knob to
survey a block of territory between the main range of the
Appalachians and the Blue Ridge to the east, including the
drainage areas of the Nolichucky and French Broad Rivers.[6]
What was done thereafter represented a broadening and
lengthening of these first lines of march. Bien continued northeastward into Virginia, first west and then east of the Blue
Ridge, teaming up during the middle and late 1880's with a
party which had been advancing from Cumberland, Maryland,
since 1883. Also in 1883 a campaign to map West Virginia
was initiated, and men were sent into the country between
the Big Sandy River and the Kanawha River. Farther south,
Yeates and others mapped eastern Kentucky—geographically
speaking, the Cumberland Plateau—while for three years
Pearson recorded topography in the mountain, valley, and
plateau regions of Tennessee. Large upland portions of three
other states, North Carolina, Georgia, and Alabama, were also

[6] W. C. Kerr to J. W. Powell, January 1, 1883, U. S. Geological Survey,
Monthly Reports, 1882, U.S. National Archives.

mapped. By the 1890's the topographers were exploring beyond the mountain system into central Alabama, the piedmont of North Carolina, and the coastal plain of Virginia.

In 1884 agreements were reached to map the five northeastern states of Massachusetts, Rhode Island, Connecticut, New York, and New Jersey. Local scientists and Survey members organized these federal-state ventures. In January 1884 H. F. Walling, hired expressly by Gannett for service as a surveyor in Massachusetts, approached Governor G. D. Robinson about mapping the state. Robinson thought well of Walling's idea and by incorporating it into his gubernatorial message opened the way for the first negotiations.[7] Five years later W. H. Brewer of the Yale Sheffield Scientific School informed Powell that "a bill has been introduced into our state legislature looking towards a topographical survey of the state by your department." In the spring of that year (1889) the legislature of Connecticut authorized cooperation.[8] In 1884 S. F. Peckham, a chemist and special agent on petroleum of the Tenth Census, lobbied to persuade the Rhode Island assembly to agree to have the state mapped, and two years later Walling appeared in Providence before a legislative finance committee.

To gain the approval of state legislatures for mapping required strategy, because they were dominated by a rural element. In Connecticut, Brewer wanted arguments for a topographical survey which would impress an honest and moderately intelligent legislature. He told Powell that this body was composed almost entirely of new members "whose ancestors, many of them, lived and prospered 250 years *without* any such a survey. When I tell them that we have a better map of the Moon than we have of Connecticut . . . they don't dispute me, but that doesn't convince them."[9]

In another small seaboard state the agrarians blocked au-

[7] H. F. Walling to J. W. Powell, January 8, 14, 1884, U. S. Geological Survey, Letters Received, 1884.
[8] W. H. Brewer to J. W. Powell, March 8, 1889, *ibid.*, 1889.
[9] *Ibid.*

thorization for mapping. A. T. Neale of the Delaware Agricultural Experiment Station wrote in April 1891 that a resolution of cooperation had passed the legislature and he needed advice. He cautioned Powell against thinking that only the details of administration remained to be worked out. Certain Delaware political leaders were pressing the state senators to reconsider their action, claiming that the people had not been informed regarding the utility of the cooperative venture. Apparently unfavorable reaction won out, for a month later Neale reported his defeat, blaming the farmers' ignorance concerning the virtues of a topographical survey.[10]

Within the "cooperation" agreements or joint programs Powell was the dominating figure. He first showed his strong hand in Massachusetts when Governor Robinson was selecting the commission to negotiate with the federal bureau. The law required Robinson to appoint three persons "qualified by education and experience in topographical science."[11] In March 1884 Powell proposed Shaler of Harvard and President F. A. Walker of Massachusetts Institute of Technology; and, fearing a political appointment, in June he asked for another scientist from one of these colleges. Only in this third appointment was Powell frustrated. The third place went to H. L. Whiting, a member of the Coast and Geodetic Survey. Once formed, the commission's influence was minor, although it was matching funds dollar for dollar up to $40,000. In July it agreed to a plan of operations which Powell had formulated in March, stipulating such minutae as cost, scale, pace, and arrangements for printing and engraving. The commission retained the right to inspect results and even persuaded the Survey to map in several directions during the first season so that the critique would cover typical landscapes. Within a year the commission-

10 A. T. Neale to J. W. Powell, April 18, May 23, 1891, *ibid.*, 1891.
11 "Report of the Commissioners of State Topographical Survey for a Part of the Year 1884," in Massachusetts, *Reports of Topographical Survey Commission and Town Boundary Triangulation of Massachusetts, 1884-1895* (Boston, 1895), 3.

ers announced that they were relinquishing their supervisory role, a promise which Walker and Shaler kept. When Whiting, the third commissioner, sought to influence further the tempo and organization of the work, his counsel was ignored. Powell and Gannett were too set in their original plans. When the director could not have his own way, he refused to participate in cooperative projects. Arrangements for a joint survey in New York were delayed four years because the legislature wished to specify terms. "I do not care . . . to make any tender for cooperation whatsoever," was Powell's decisive answer.[12]

The coordinating commission in Rhode Island had to fight for even a little control. In 1888 Winslow Upton, a professor of astronomy at Brown University, complained in a letter to Powell that topographical parties were not conferring with the commission. Powell told Upton the Geological Survey had mapped hundreds of thousands of square miles, that in the course of this experience it had developed "special" topographic and cartographic methods, and that these methods assured "accurate work, characteristic representation, and economic execution." Powell threatened to withdraw if the commission did not leave him free to plan and to execute the Survey work, to select men, and to determine methods for constructing the map. After two days Powell wrote again saying if the commissioners would withdraw their letter, he would give them full information about the character and progress of the mapping. Upton answered with dignity, assuring Powell that no one had intended to be rude or dictatorial. His letter was meant to convey "a most courteous protest"[13] against a procedure which hampered the state representatives. The commissioners understood perfectly that Powell must plan and execute the topography. At the same time they had assumed a responsibility under the articles of agreement to observe and

[12] J. W. Powell to Verplanck Colvin, January 10, 1888, U. S. Geological Survey, Letters Sent, 1888.
[13] Winslow Upton to J. W. Powell, June 22, 1888, U. S. Geological Survey, Letters Received, 1888.

check the mapping, so they must know the location of the field parties. For this they established an office in Providence where federal and state officials met, left addresses and field sheets, and stored equipment. Thereafter the mapping in Rhode Island continued uneventfully.

Topographers laid the foundation for further work in economic geology. In Colorado they moved from the first station at Leadville to the Ten Mile mining district (Summit County) and then to several points in Custer County—Silver Cliff, Rosita, and Querida. Next they moved north to map the coal outcrops near Golden and Denver and then to the Elk Mountains farther west. In 1882 they went to California to make detailed surveys of four quicksilver districts. When geologists entered the gold belt of California in the mid-eighties, they found the topographers had arrived first. East of the Mississippi topographers worked where coal and iron ore resources were known to exist. More directly linked to pure science were surveys at the lava beds and volcanic cones of northern California and southern Oregon, the alluvial region of Louisiana, Yellowstone National Park, and several glaciated areas in Wisconsin and Iowa.

The maps prepared by the topographic division brought professional admiration and gave support to the engineers of industrial America. When Emmanuel de Margerie, a French geologist and topographer, reviewed a broad selection of Survey maps, he praised the quality of the work of five topographers, calling maps by H. M. Wilson of Marsh Pass and Canyon de Chelly in Arizona "truly admirable." The scale was small, the pace of surveying had been very rapid, and much had had to be sketched in with the eye; nevertheless, De Margerie said he could understand the landscape forms better than from maps produced by "our detailed European Surveys." He praised Eugene Ricksecker's penwork on the

Long Valley sheet in Nevada and L. C. Fletcher and W. T. Griswold, for the Harrisonburg sheet of Virginia.[14] De Margerie also admired W. D. Johnson's mapping in Massachusetts.

Southern railroad builders were the first industrialists to gain practical benefit from the maps of the Survey. By 1887 at a time when a score of new lines were under construction between Appalachian coalfields and the seaboard or the Ohio River 3,500 topographical sheets had been distributed to companies. One railroad official said the Survey maps had saved his company at least $10,000 in preliminary exploration for a railroad between South Carolina and Ohio.[15] Civil engineers in the northeast, who were building water systems, underground railways, interurban lines, and highways for the new urban centers, learned of the topographical maps and gratefully used them. The city of Waterbury, Connecticut, was seeking a new water supply when its engineer saw the Survey sheets of Naugatuck Valley, which he said "would be of the greatest value." The chief engineer of the Massachusetts State Board of Health praised such maps because they enabled him to proceed more effectively in fighting water pollution. Also praising the maps' utility was the chief engineer for the Croton Aqueduct of New York City. In 1894 professional appreciation was shown in a resolution by the American Society of Civil Engineers asking that the state legislature of New York continue cooperation with the national bureau.[16]

Unfortunately, the topographic branch's work can be critisized in some aspects. Powell's desire to complete the map in one generation forced the topographers to move at a pace which undermined their craftsmanship. According to W. D. Johnson, speed seemed to be "an unwritten law" of the

14 Emmanuel de Margerie to J. W. Powell, February 21, 1890, U.S. Geological Survey, Letters Received, 1890.
15 *Science*, X (1887), 37.
16 "Abstract of Reports, Letters, Clippings, Indorsements, Resolutions, Petitions, and Requests, Showing the Demand for the Topographical Work of the U.S. Geological Survey," U.S., Senate Doc. No. 136, 57th Cong., 1st Sess., 11, 26, 27, 39, 40.

Survey. A typical result was the Fort Scott sheet of Allen
County in southeastern Kansas, which Robert Hay, author
of two Survey bulletins, found full of errors.[17] Hay cited
several towns mapped a mile or more out of position, and he
marked roads and railroads which were omitted or incorrectly
located. Among the missing waterways were a creek five or six
miles long and a river bend one-quarter of a mile across.
Contour lines had been put in so hurriedly that numerous
well-known and obvious hillocks and mounds were omitted.
Because of their small scale the Kansas sheets were not much
help to Hay, who was examining gas-yielding and oil-bearing
rocks. The 50-foot contour interval was unsatisfactory for so
level a country where the inclination of strata averaged 8
to 12 feet per mile and the thickness of formations 12 to 48
feet. Contour lines which recorded only the changes above 50
feet missed much of the dip and elevation in the landscape.[18]

The erroneous maps discredited the Survey, as W. D. Johnson learned when he went to California in 1891 to direct the
topographic work. Johnson wanted a federal-state agreement
like the one in Massachusetts, but he encountered opposition
from civil engineers who held a low opinion of the Survey.
These engineers doubted the bureau's ability to make good
maps, especially at the cost per square mile usually proposed. Also, they feared that if it ever should undertake a
genuinely scientific operation, the Survey would not maintain
high standards, "but would progressively cheapen the work."[19]
These critics had the backing of Coast Survey scientists in
California. George Davidson, the senior member there of the
Coast Survey and an influential figure locally, argued that the
state should wait and cooperate with the Coast Survey which,

[17] Robert Hay to W J McGee, July 14, 1886, W J McGee Papers,
Library of Congress.
  In another letter Hay marked the drainage and cultural errors in Jasper
County (Missouri) on the Joplin sheet. Robert Hay to W J McGee,
August 12, 1886, ibid.
[18] Robert Hay to W J McGee, December 3, 1886, ibid.
[19] W. D. Johnson to W J McGee, December 22, 1892, ibid.

having "a corps of professional map makers," would do a
scientific job "of guaranteed accuracy." Johnson repudiated
the Survey's "wretched pieces" on the Cascade Range and in
the gold fields, urging the Survey scientists to forget "prece-
dents in the expense account," to show itself willing to pay
for good science, and to concentrate upon its maps with the
largest scale (one mile to the inch), perfecting them and keeping within the budget by reducing coverage.[20] The prevalent
distrust of Powell would then subside, and scientists would
stop saying that his maps were makeshift, put up for geological use only.

The performance of the topographical division during
Powell's regime alternated between achievement and failure.
This division was perhaps the most popular in the early
Survey. In two years (1887-1888) 100,000 copies of its topographical sheets were distributed by the Massachusetts author-
ities. Though criticized publicly, the hasty, inaccurate work
never provoked a political reaction. However, this success
cannot be an apology for poor science, and the topographical
division was the only division of the early Survey responsible
for producing any quantity of inaccurate work.

20 *Ibid.*, January 12, 1893.

Chapter Six

THE NEW POSITION OF PRACTICAL SCIENCE

An important change in the practical science of the Survey was made after 1882. Clarence King, the first director, had organized his bureau around western mining studies, but after his resignation and the return to multiple science under Powell these practical studies lost their preeminence. Marking most decisively the trend away from King's policy was the dismantling of the regional framework for field operations. In reaction the western mining geologists formed an opposition group to Powell and his policies, and factionalism became a salient feature of the Survey. There was no decline, however, in the quality of findings from practical science. The Emmons volume on Leadville was significant intellectually, and the field work in the copper and iron ore regions of Lake Superior resulted in creditable publications. The division of statistics and technology, authorized in 1882, was active. Overall, the Survey demonstrated its power for economic advancement, thus strengthening its position as a public agency. Relations with state geological surveys left little doubt that the new national bureau now overshadowed the older state organizations.

The battle between the mining geologists and Powell focused on the Survey's division of the Rocky Mountains, where King and Emmons planned for increased field work and more monographs on western mining camps. In the summer of 1884 Powell began the devolution of the division by transferring topographer Anton Karl to Massachusetts where the cooperative agreement had just been signed. In August, Karl went into the field west of the Connecticut River, leaving unfinished business in Colorado at Silver Cliff in the Wet Mountain Valley of Custer County, at Crested Butte in the Elk Mountains of Gunnison County, and in the Denver coal basin (an area of 1,000 square miles surrounding the capital). Emmons regarded Karl's transfer as a mortal threat to his whole division. Topography was the key to the division's scientific activity, and Karl's transfer suggested that those dozens of mining areas planned for study by him and his staff would never be seen. Powell said that Gannett of the division of geography would provide replacement topographers, but Emmons replied that this would undermine the philosophy of regional autonomy. The mapping in the Rocky Mountains, he told the director, differed from the general topographic work of the Survey because it applied to minute areas and was specifically designed to serve mining geology. Whoever examined a mining district must have charge of the mapping there as he alone would be competent to decide how the topography should be laid down and how it should be corrected and amplified as the geological studies progressed.[1]

Powell's answer charged Emmons with failure to concentrate on his assigned task. Emmons had spent five years at Leadville, and the monograph was still unfinished. Meanwhile, he had entered three or four new and complex fields, each calling for several complete lines of work.[2] Powell advised that the Leadville study be completed and that research at the other places be done one project at a time. He then allotted $20,000 to the division of the Rocky Mountains for the fiscal year 1884-1885, which was $8,000 less than the previous year. Emmons maintained that the inadequate budget, rather than his lack of discipline, caused the slowdown. With-

[1] S. F. Emmons to J. W. Powell, July 17, 1884, U. S. Geological Survey, Letters Received, 1884.
[2] J. W. Powell to S. F. Emmons, July 25, 1884, *ibid.*, Letters Sent, 1884.

out money, he said, the personnel for the different mining districts could not be provided, and he himself was lost in details of administration. With 50 percent more funds the division could have accomplished twice as much research, he added.[3]

Powell was adamant and in the following years widened the retrenchment policy against the Rocky Mountain division. No new districts were visited, Emmons went into the field less frequently (he spent the summers of 1885 and 1886 on the Leadville manuscript), the division was compelled to rely heavily upon the Hayden atlas for topography, and the personnel loss accelerated. W. F. Hildebrand, the division's chief chemist, returned to Washington in 1885, and G. H. Eldridge, one of the assistant geologists, went to Florida to do phosphate studies in 1891. But the most indicative action of deemphasis was the closing of the Denver office in 1887.

When the fatal order was telegraphed from Washington in October 1887, Emmons protested vigorously. He wanted Powell to visit the Denver office personally (which he had never done) and to consult local persons on the advantages of the division to the mining interests.[4] A regional staff made communication easier between science and mining, transforming an impersonal and distant government bureau into an intimate and respected part of the Colorado scene. The laboratory, which had gained an international reputation through the establishment of a new rock species (Hypersthene-Andesite), exemplified the rapport with local interests. Its presence prompted mining people to send interesting substances for analysis, and led mine owners and operators to pay more attention to science.[5]

Doubtless, Emmons inspired the public reaction to the clos-

---

[3] S. F. Emmons to J. W. Powell, August 1, 1884, *ibid.*, Letters Received, 1884.

[4] S. F. Emmons to J. W. Powell, November, 1887, *ibid.*, 1887, No. 2148.

[5] *Ibid.* The species discovery appeared as Bulletin No. One of the Survey. Whitman Cross, *On Hypersthene-Andesite and on Triclinic Pyroxene in Augitic Rocks* (Washington, 1883).

ing. He and his staff belonged to the Colorado Scientific Society, a group of professionals connected with mines and smelting works. This society passed a resolution against Powell's order, and the Denver Chamber of Commerce dispatched a petition of protest signed by 150 persons and praising the Survey's "timely and important papers . . . on current mining topics" in the reports on Virginia City, Leadville, Eureka (Nevada), and the mines near Lake Superior.[6] G. G. Symes, congressman from Colorado, said the Denver office was a regional clearing house for mining and scientific groups and charged that its elimination was part of a general policy to reduce the small sum of money set aside by the Survey for practical geology in the mining regions.[7] Two years ago, Symes wrote, he had spoken and voted against a motion to reduce the Survey's appropriation. If the Denver office were removed, would not the people of Colorado turn their backs on the Survey?

These complaints and threats caused Director Powell to hesitate, and for about six months the closing of the office was not definite. In February 1888 Emmons wanted to know whether he should unpack the equipment which had arrived from Denver. As late as July 1888 he was inquiring about a return. The overhead at Denver could be justified, he wrote, if studies were begun at Aspen, Colorado, and Butte, Montana.[8] In the end neither he nor the mining interests of Colorado swayed Powell, and the Denver office closed, dramatizing the western mining element's loss of primacy in Powell's national, diversified organization.

That same year Emmons' personal research, *Geology and Mining Industry of Leadville, Colorado,* was issued from the Government Printing Office, fulfilling his earlier promise of

[6] Petition and Protest of the Denver Chamber of Commerce, December 31, 1887, U.S. Geological Survey, Letters Received, 1888.

[7] G. G. Symes to J. W. Powell, January 18, 1888, *ibid.*

[8] S. F. Emmons to J. W. Powell, February 3, 1888, *ibid.*

an intelligent guide to the ore deposits at Leadville. Originally, miners had discovered valuable silver and lead in a blue dolomitic limestone at or near its contact with white porphyry, an igneous rock. Emmons identified this zone as the preeminent source of the ore. Subsequently, however, miners uncovered large mineral deposits in an underlying white limestone, which was penetrated by or lay close to another igneous rock called gray porphyry. This discovery was called the "second contact."[9] Both ore-bearing strata were crossed and dislocated by large faults. Emmons measured the displacement and located in their fullest extent the two contacts where the ore was concentrated—along the blue limestone and the white porphyry and along the white limestone and the gray porphyry.

Emmons' *Leadville* revolutionized the influence of geology in Colorado mining. His maps were hung in the post office, and his name became well-known to miners, who marvelled at the number of ore chutes he had discovered. The local newspaper reported that prospectors in their search of ore deposits were abandoning popular methods and were studying geological structure instead. The climax of the community appreciation came in August 1890 when 30 men representing the city, the mines, and the press of Leadville paid Emmons tribute with a banquet. There was general agreement on this occasion that his *magnum opus* had brought Leadville to its prosperous condition. One speaker said that he was doing for the miner what the astronomer and the Coast Survey did for the mariner. A year later, 50 managers and owners in Aspen, Colorado, impressed by the research at Leadville, petitioned for government geologists to study their mines.[10]

[9] *Geology and Mining Industry of Leadville, Colorado, with Atlas* (Washington, 1888), 540-42. On the title page of this volume the date of publication is given as 1886. For a later description and appraisal of Emmons' discovery, see T. A. Rickard, *A History of American Mining*, 132.

[10] Leadville *Herald Democrat*, August 9, 1890, Scrapbook, Emmons Papers, Library of Congress. Petition from Aspen, Colorado, June 1, 1891, U. S. Geological Survey, Letters Received, 1891.

Emmons also made progress in theory. He convinced the scientific world that the ore deposits at Leadville were primarily a replacement for blue or white limestone, countering the traditional view that ore formation in limestone required a preexisting open cavity which vein material coming from elsewhere occupied. He was correct, but less original, in his conclusion that the minerals replacing the limestone were precipitated from aqueous solution. The aqueous solution he traced back to atmospheric waters circulating underground and to the metallic content of the porphyries. Today's geologists much prefer the explanation that the waters were magmatic in origin, arising from molten rock material deep in the earth's interior. As they left the magma chamber, they carried valuable minerals in solution. These waters spread along the strata at favorable places, particularly along limestone beds beneath impervious covers of porphyry.

Becker's volume on the Comstock Lode was another accomplishment of the Survey's practical science branch. Mine operators in the Comstock district regarded the volume highly and consulted it frequently. Through careful microscopic study Becker distinguished many rock species and for the first time identified the sequence of rocks in detail. He demonstrated convincingly that intense heat in the lode came from ascending waters.[11] Becker also made a collateral study on quicksilver in California, which was so important in the metallurgy of the Comstock ores.[12]

Becker disagreed with Powell over the direction and scope of future research. In California Becker planned to devote his time to abstruse problems in physics and chemistry, while Powell wanted mapping of mineral resources emphasized. In 1884 after a year at the quicksilver mines Becker said he would next like to map a geological belt across the Coast Range

---

[11] Waldemar Lindgren, *Mineral Deposits,* 3rd ed. (New York, 1928), 89.
[12] *Geology of the Quicksilver Deposits of the Pacific Slope, with an Atlas* (Washington, 1888).

either just south of Clear Lake or between Fort Tejon and
the coast. Immediately Powell inquired about "your desire
. . . when you first went to California . . . to take up work
on the gold gravels as a special study, and the structure of
the Sierra Nevada as a general study."[13] The topographers
were preparing maps of both places and had already spent
considerable money, and a shift now meant a delay of several
years until the base mapping could be done with the money
available. The director criticized the sectional approach to
the Coast Range, saying unequal displacement, masking by
other formations, and irregular strata were likely to be overlooked. Powell said the Coast Range must be examined as a
whole, as a province; only then could its important external
relations be appreciated—relations with the Sierra Nevada
on the east and the extinct volcanoes to the north. Powell
admitted that ideally the gold gravels came after the Coast
Range and the Sierra, but that so painstaking a method of
study belonged to another generation of geologists. He urged
Becker to concentrate on the quicksilver work, promising that
when the book was completed "you and I will not be long in
reaching a conclusion as to the next best field, especially as
I shall leave it to a large extent to your own judgment."[14]

In March 1885 Becker picked the gold gravels, a decision
which dismayed the Washington office. He proposed not simply the gold belt proper, that "narrow tongue of country"
averaging 25 to 30 miles in width and stretching north to
Nevada City, but an area 12,000 miles square on the west
flank of the Sierra Nevada.[15] Becker proposed to study super-
ficial deposits, quartz veins, structural geology, metamorphism,
the lithology of rocks without regular form, and glacial
phenomena. He anticipated four monographs and numerous

13 J. W. Powell to G. F. Becker, June 5, 1884, U. S. Geological Survey,
Letters Sent, 1884.
14 J. W. Powell to G. F. Becker, July 25, 1884, *ibid.*
15 G. F. Becker to J. W. Powell, March 16, 1885, U. S. Geological Survey,
Letters Received, 1885.

maps on the scale of two inches to the mile. But Powell thought the proposal impractical.[16] Structure by itself was one field, the metamorphic rocks another, and the gold gravels alone would take many years, the director said. He dismissed the topographical maps on the scale of two inches to the mile as too costly.

The exchange between field geologist and director then ended, and Becker began work on the problem of rock masses under intense stress (in the Sierra Nevada), the shape of volcanic cones, the earth's interior, and other theoretical questions. He left mapping of geological strata to his assistants, one of whom, H. W. Turner, was showing "great ability as an observer" in 1884. Becker wanted another such helper—"some young graduate or student from a foreign mining school who feels more attracted by geology than by professional mining."[17] Several months later W. M. Davis recommended Waldemar Lindgren because of his "high standing at Freiberg," his knowledge of German, English, and Spanish, his intimate acquaintance with minerals and rocks, and his service with the Northern Transcontinental Survey.[18] Lindgren and Turner labored for years on the gold gravels of California and published a dozen or more folios in the geologic atlas, all done on the smaller scale favored by Powell.

Powell's administration of the division of statistics and technology was another source of friction. In 1882 Becker pleaded with the director not to omit the appropriation for this popular work. "I believe," he wrote, "that it is only on condition of doing something of the kind that the Survey will be permitted to become a permanent institution."[19] In 1883 Emmons went directly to Congress: "Powell is very much inclined to

16 J. W. Powell to G. F. Becker, March 25, 1885, *ibid.*, Letters Sent, 1885.

17 G. F. Becker to J. W. Powell, May 4, 1884, U. S. Geological Survey, Letters Received, 1884.

18 W. M. Davis to J. W. Powell, July 17, 1884, Waldemar Lindgren to G. F. Becker, October 18, 1884, *ibid.*

19 G. F. Becker to J. W. Powell, July 4, 1882, U. S. Geological Survey, Letters Received, 1882.

throw over the statistics altogether," he wrote Becker; "I tried to put a block in his wheel in that respect when I was in Washington."[20] The division was discontinued for a year and revived in 1884, greatly to Becker's delight.

Annually this division published *Mineral Resources of the United States*, a volume giving figures on important products and descriptions of their discovery and processing. The authors devoted a separate article to each mineral. Contributors were editors of trade journals, mining engineers, metallurgists, manufacturers, and professors. J. D. Weeks of the *American Manufacturer*, for example, reported on coke after corresponding with 250 producers. Weeks included the number of ovens, and purity, composition, and price of the product, the production and consumption.[21] *Mineral Resources* won great renown, and in sales it led all other publications of the Survey.

Intellectual and practical success did not reduce the mining geologists' ill-feeling toward Powell. Led by Emmons and Becker, they were a disgruntled element which remembered when King was director and imagined what they could do if he still were director. Persons in this faction tended to come from old, eastern families, to have wealth, to be conservative and German-trained. They disliked Gilbert, who was chief geologist, and McGee, Powell's alter ego. Emmons said that Gilbert was not familiar with economic geology and suppressed rather than encouraged this important branch of knowledge. Hence, if an economic geologist wanted authorization or publication for some research, he must first fight delays in Gilbert's office before struggling with the director himself. McGee, in the opinion of this group, lacked the judgment and ability required for his high position. Understandably an opposing clique formed, whose supporters were either poor or without eastern and foreign scholastic training. They rallied

20 S. F. Emmons to G. F. Becker, May 30, 1883, Becker Papers.
21 J. D. Weeks, "The Manufacture of Coke," *Mineral Resources of the United States, Calendar Year 1885* (Washington, 1886), 74-129.

around "the Great Basin lunch mess," a congenial if exclusive group which spent the noon hour together.[22] McGee was a leading spirit, and Gilbert and topographer Johnson also were prominent. This second faction was closer to the director, who shared their origins and social status. The other side charged favoritism in promotions. Bailey Willis, who joined "the Great Basin lunch mess," was better paid and moved ahead faster than did Cross or Eldridge of the Rocky Mountain division. J. S. Diller was placed in charge of petrology, although Cross and Iddings held seniority and were internationally known.[23] Diller was zealous, Emmons admitted, but less brilliant and accurate. In tolerating this internal strife Powell revealed a weakness in proper institutional management. And far worse, he risked the danger that in their discontent the mining geologists would make an alliance with politicians desirous of ruining the Survey.[24]

Once again scientists at the University of Wisconsin led the national bureau into a new field, this time the copper and iron ore region of Lake Superior. Professors R. D. Irving and C. R. Van Hise directed the federal research, which expanded enormously the knowledge of pre-Cambrian rocks. Irving prepared a monograph on the copper-bearing series in northern Michigan. He proposed the Keweenawan system, a large group of pre-Cambrian formations which he named after Keweenaw Point, the eastward tending peninsula of Lake Superior's southern shore. First, he isolated a lower or

[22] W. M. Davis, *Biographical Memoir: Grove Karl Gilbert, 1843-1918,* Memoirs of the National Academy of Sciences, XXI (1927), 122-23.

[23] Iddings published on the igneous rocks of Eureka, Nevada, and Yellowstone Park. J. P. Iddings, "Microscopical Petrography of the Eruptive Rocks . . ." in Arnold Hague, *Geology of the Eureka District, Nevada* (Washington, 1892). Arnold Hague, J. P. Iddings and others, *Geology of the Yellowstone National Park: Part II, Descriptive Geology, Petrography, and Paleontology* (Washington, 1899).

[24] See below, p. 212.

earlier series of lava flows which originated the valuable copper deposits. Then he showed that structurally these Keweenawan lavas interbedded with an upper series of red sandstone and shales which came afterward and were, for the most part, materials eroded from lava fields.[25] After publication of the manuscript in 1882, Irving began studying on the iron ore deposits, which were also in the pre-Cambrian, when he died unexpectedly in 1888, leaving Van Hise to head the Lake Superior division. In the geological column the pre-Cambrian group containing the iron ore deposits was placed earlier than Irving's Keweenawan system and separated from the Keweenawan by a pronounced unconformity. Van Hise and his assistants established the Penokee and Marquette series, two sequences of sedimentary formations which contained beds of cherty iron carbonate, the source of the mineral wealth. F. W. Rhinelander, president of the Milwaukee, Lake Shore and Western Railroad, was enthusiastic about the findings, and one miner compared Van Hise to Emmons in intellectual powers.[26] Indeed, the Lake Superior division made great progress in accounting for the fabulous ore, saying that originally the "iron formation" had been laid down by sedimentation and then enriched through weathering.[27]

This specific accomplishment did not lead, however, to a general theory applying to all conditions of ore deposition. Van Hise adopted the extreme view that all ore deposits were primarily the result of atmospheric water circulating underground, an opinion that many scientists then and now find

25 *The Copper-Bearing Rocks of Lake Superior* (Washington, 1883), Chapters II, IX, X.

26 F. W. Rhinelander to C. R. Van Hise, October 28, 1891, J. R. Finlay to C. R. Van Hise, April 15, 1892, State Historical Society of Wisconsin, C. R. Van Hise Papers.
Van Hise mourned the delay of two and one-half years before publication, which lessened considerably the "directive" value of the Penokee report. C. R. Van Hise to G. K. Gilbert, December 9, 1891, *ibid.*

27 C. R. Van Hise, "The Iron-Ore Deposits of the Lake Superior Region," U.S.G.S. *Twenty-first Annual Report* (Washington, 1900), Part III, 323-26.

unacceptable. The current trend of scientific knowledge also has lessened the permanent contribution of these men to the general geology of the Lake Superior region. For decades the Geological Survey has not used the Van Hise group's division of pre-Cambrian time into Algonkian and Archean eras, and after 60 years geologists are discarding Van Hise's term Huronian to designate the pre-Cambrian sequence of rocks in Michigan and Wisconsin, including the iron formations.[28]

When Survey geologists entered the mountains of the South, organized as the division of the Appalachians, they did not claim to be the first of their profession there. Since the beginning of modern geology this region had been regarded as one of the most remarkable mountain provinces in the world. Its unusual symmetry and vastness made it a type structure. Much had been written about this region, but this knowledge had yet to be presented in the graphic form of geological maps with topographical foundations. Using Gannett's product, Gilbert, chief of the division, planned zones 20 miles wide for geological surveying across the mountain chain from northwest to southeast. Three such zones or belts were actually mapped—one from Cumberland, Maryland, southeast across the Blue Ridge; another from Cumberland Gap, Tennessee, to Asheville, North Carolina; and a third from the plateau of Alabama southeast to beyond Rome, Georgia. This mapping helped Gilbert and his colleagues make subdivisions of the long time scale which they had to construct and also to approach the principal theoretical problem, the mechanics of mountain building. After 1888 the point of emphasis in this large province became clear. According to Bailey Willis, now chief of the division, the region divided itself naturally into an eastern district—the Blue Ridge and the North Carolina mountains—and a western district—the Cumberland Plateau

---

[28] Harold L. James, *Stratigraphy of Pre-Keweenawan Rocks in Parts of Northern Michigan*, Geological Survey Professional Paper No. 314-C (Washington, 1958), 28-30, 33-35.

and the Appalachian Valley areas. The decisive attraction of the western district was the Appalachian coalfield. Willis sent his geologists to the western district for the areal mapping— into northeastern Alabama and Georgia, eastern Tennessee and Kentucky, western Virginia and Maryland, and several parts of West Virginia. The geologic atlas carried many folios from these places.

Dual mapping takes time and southerners were impatient. To mollify them the Survey undertook special or interim studies. I. C. White, professor at the University of West Virginia, gave Powell a bulletin on bituminous coal sections in Pennsylvania, Ohio, and West Virginia. Later Marius Campbell brought out a bulletin on the Big Stone Gap coalfield in Virginia and Kentucky. The phosphate deposits of Florida were also primary interests of the Survey. Powell used paleontologist Dall, who developed his knowledge of phosphates and published about them in local newspapers. In 1891 Eldridge, coming from Colorado, organized a division for study of these deposits.[29]

Powell often said that a division of labor guided federal relations with the state geological surveys. The national bureau mapped physical features and ascertained geological structure, and then the state organizations built economic research on these foundations. He quoted the Act of 1879, which authorized the Survey to examine the geological structure, mineral resources, and products of the national domain; in other words, "to do all classes of geologic work on the national domain." The clause in the Act of 1882, bringing the Survey into the states, restricted it to "a particular class of work," namely "to continue the preparation of a geological map of the United States." This clause referred to structural

29 "Report of Mr. George H. Eldridge," U.S.G.S. *Twelfth Annual Report* (Washington, 1891), 82-84.

and general geology, not economic studies, which the states themselves must initiate. The events between 1879 and 1882 do not bear out Powell's gloss of fundamental law. People liked what the bureau had been doing in the West and imagined it working the same way in the East. Nevertheless, Powell used the distinction. In Alabama, E. A. Smith, receiving $50,000 from the state legislature, planned to spend most of the money on coal and iron research. Powell volunteered his topographers and promised finished maps, sending a collector to help with the geology and paleontology.[30] The arrangement with New Jersey was more complicated. State topographers constructed maps which were paid for by the United States Survey. In geology the national government scientists mapped the crystalline and metamorphic rocks with their deposits of iron and zinc, and the states plotted the superficial formations from which "the soils . . . are largely derived."[31] The federal bureau published the local research in paleontology.

In 1889 when the legislature of Missouri founded a geological survey, Powell organized a division of zinc to operate near Joplin. This violation of his own rule followed a peremptory order from Secretary of the Interior J. W. Noble to investigate mineral deposits in Missouri. Then W. P. Jenney, chief of the division of zinc, quarreled with Arthur Winslow of the state survey, who then withdrew a geologist assigned to help Jenney. Simultaneously, the Washington office said they had misplaced faith in Jenney, who showed himself too exuberant in theory and unable to concentrate on specific topics. No one wanted to labor over his reports, nor could anyone reasonably ask the state survey in Missouri to publish

[30] J. W. Powell to E. A. Smith, April 18, 1883, U. S. Geological Survey, Letters Sent, 1883; E. A. Smith to J. W. Powell, February 21, April 14, 22, 1883, November 29, 1884, February 16, 1891, U. S. Geological Survey, Letters Received, 1883, 1884, 1891.

[31] "Report of the Director," U.S.G.S. *Thirteenth Annual Report,* 12. J. W. Powell to S. B. Dod, October 16, 1890, U. S. Geological Survey, Letters Sent, 1890.

them as they were submitted. This painful and unproductive relationship was terminated in 1892 when the division of zinc did not survive the appropriations reduction of that year.[32]

With the state survey of Minnesota the Geological Survey had no understanding. N. H. Winchell, the state director, unlike most state geologists, would not solicit federal money, and nothing about the U. S. Geological Survey in Minnesota pleased him. Its presence raised the threat that the research by Irving might make it "appear unnecessary and useless" for him to map the same areas, thus circumscribing his bureau and bringing it eventually "to an inglorious termination." He had not learned of the Survey's entry into Minnesota until many months after it had happened, and he resented Powell's hiring of a man whom Winchell had fired—C. W. Hall of the University of Minnesota. Finally, Winchell had professional objections to the "hasty and ill considered observations" of Irving on the geology of the Lake Superior region.[33] Winchell wanted all scientific studies in Minnesota to be his responsibility. He suggested letting Minnesota become the headquarters of the national survey for the district of the upper Mississippi and letting the state survey direct the regional fieldwork of the national bureau. Powell never had agreed to anything remotely approaching this kind of "cooperation," so he simply ignored the proposal, which he actually had invited by asking Winchell for written criticisms of the Geological Survey during a conference. The director could adopt this attitude because, following Irving and Van Hise, he held Winchell's science in contempt.

It is interesting to compare federal-state experience in both geology and topography with the fears expressed during the congressional debates in 1879 and 1882. History did not substantiate Dana and Reagan's accusation of imperialism. The

[32] S. F. Emmons to C. D. Walcott, May 19, 1893, U. S. Geological Survey, Letters Received, 1893.
[33] N. H. Winchell to J. W. Powell, April 30, 1883, *ibid.*, 1883.

national bureau stayed out of Minnesota for years because of hostile feeling in that state. Where the state university wanted to control all geological studies, as in Kansas, scientists of the Survey could not arrange a joint effort.[34] In Alabama Powell promised E. A. Smith, the state geologist, that he would undertake no geology in that state without first consulting Smith.[35] When the Survey entered states, it often stimulated local activity, rather than eliminating it. The topographical commissions of New England and the middle states would not have existed in the absence of Powell and his ambition for a national map. The fears of Dana and Reagan make sense if the rights of the states meant, as it did for these two men, local leadership and accomplishment in science. They interpreted the rise of a national survey as threatening this tradition, and in practice Powell's Survey did make the state bureaus look insignificant. Nor were local scientists deceived by the word "cooperation."

In a vice-presidential address before the American Association for the Advancement of Science in 1890, J. C. Branner, state geologist of Arkansas, belittled the idea of a geological partnership between states and the Union. He said the Survey did not cooperate closely with state surveys, commenting that in most cases one agency knew little of what the other was doing. Branner cited one state—clearly Texas—"where the national survey carried its topographic work forward without any reference to what the state [geological] survey needed, for it didn't know the state survey's needs, and when, almost by accident, the state survey learned of the government work, that work had gone too far to be modified to suit the needs of the state survey."[36]

34 A. H. Thompson to J. W. Powell, January 6, 1888, *ibid.*, 1888.

35 J. W. Powell to E. A. Smith, April 18, 1883, U. S. Geological Survey, Letters Sent, 1883.

36 J. C. Branner, "The Relations of the State and National Geological Surveys to Each Other and to the Geologists of the Country," *American Geologist,* VI (1890), 298.

Branner was only acknowledging a powerful trend in American history. First the idea of a unified nation had been justified during four years of war. The resolution of the political crisis encouraged nationalizing of business and industry. A parallel development was the shift in the balance of power from local to national science.

Chapter Seven

CONGRESS GRANTS PERMANENCE, 1886

The supreme crisis for the Powell regime came in the mid-eighties with an investigation of the Survey by Congress, which ended after 18 months with recognition of the Survey as a permanent institution of the federal government. The phenomenal growth of the bureau prompted congressional attention. The scientific staff had increased from 40 to 200, and annual expenditures stood at $500,000, King's ideal goal in 1879. Once aroused, Congress' curiosity was stimulated further by the discovery that an important part of government science had been transformed without explicit authorization. The legislature had approved first a territorial mining bureau and then a national one, whereupon Powell used a rising budget to organize the broad Survey, which the last three chapters have described.

During the initial stage of the congressional inspection, beginning in 1884, Powell made substantial progress in persuading the politicians that his kind of Survey with its multiple science was preferable to the narrower conception which had prevailed at the founding and in 1882. When, however, Cleveland and the Democratic party came to power in 1885, the investigation took quite a different complexion. Cleveland Democracy was restrictive in its attitude toward federal bureaus, advocating frugality and hoping for as little government as possible. These views, ratified by a major political party, were more menacing to government science than the drives for economy during the 1870's. With the very existence of the Survey at stake, Powell gave an even fuller presentation of his policies, deserting the argument for limited government in science, which he had stated so eloquently in 1878 and 1879. His leadership resulted in a favorable opinion of the bureau's performance, and Congress decided to continue the Survey indefinitely, giving it the status of an established scientific agency.

The congressional method of investigation was a joint commission of six members, with Senator W. B. Allison of Iowa as chairman.[1] This commission concentrated on four scientific agencies of the federal government: the Geological Survey, the Coast and Geodetic Survey, the Signal Service of the U. S. Army, and the Hydrographic Office of the U. S. Navy. The purpose of this commission was to report on this public science in terms of economy, efficiency, legality, and utility.

Relations among the four agencies seemed to violate one or more principles of good government. The Coast and Geodetic Survey, a bureau of the Treasury Department, had always been responsible for charting the shallow waters and mapping the land adjacent to the American coast. But the actual workers on the coastal waters were naval officers and enlisted men, detached for duty outside their departments. This caused W. E. Chandler, Secretary of the Navy, to claim that he, instead of the Treasury, should command this maritime sector of the dual mapping. Also, the Navy had a Hydrographic Office which already was collecting data and taking soundings on all coasts except the American. On land the Coast Survey had ventured deep into New England and far down the Appalachians and in the 1870's had begun to locate a series of positions on the earth's surface from the Atlantic to the

[1] The full name was "The Joint Commission to Consider the Present Organization of the Signal Service. Geological Survey, Coast and Geodetic Survey, and the Hydrographic Office of the Navy Department, with a View to Secure Greater Efficiency and Economy of Administration of the Public Service in said Bureaus," U. S., Senate Misc. Doc. No. 82, 49th Cong., 1st Sess., title page. Hereinafter referred to as Record and Hearings of the Joint Commission.

Pacific. Was all this interior work legal? After the expansion of Powell's organization into the southern Appalachians, two surveys operated there, suggesting duplication or inefficiency. The Signal Service, a misleading name for the weather bureau, also suffered from civilian-military tension. Its civilian employees were in the War Department and had to submit to army discipline. Popular dissatisfaction with the bureau brought the Signal Service to congressional attention. Merchants and farmers, doubting the value of tardy or inaccurate weather predictions, complained to the lawmakers.

The commission's point of departure was the Geological Survey and Powell's ambitious drive toward a national map. For two hours during the morning of the first session—December 4, 1884—the politicians quizzed the director on his authority to operate in the eastern states. Of course Powell cited the familiar amendment of 1882, "to continue the preparation of a geological map of the United States." Senator Eugene Hale of Maine answered that this amendment did not explicitly authorize the Geological Survey to enter the eastern states and said nothing about a continental project in topography. The idea of mapping the entire United States distressed Hale, and he questioned the director: "Do you suppose that that [the 1882 clause] carried in Congress, or elsewhere, any expectation of your going on and making triangulations, topographical work, and a complete topographical map of the United States?" In reply Powell described how mapping of topography and geology had gone hand in hand since the Civil War, a partnership which the House of Representatives had discussed "elaborately and fully . . . in times past."

Hale was not appeased. He remembered Powell had drafted the 1882 amendment and accused him of deception: "why, instead of this clause 'to continue the preparation of a geological map of the United States,' did you not [explicitly] . . . provide for the geological survey of the United States, to extend its topographic and geological work into all of the States at the Government's expense; trying to make the best point of what you seem to understand as a geological map? I am familiar with the debates, and certainly it did not occur to the members of the Senate . . . that this [meant] . . . a survey of the old States. Now, in framing that language, why did you not put it in fairly?" Compelled to answer, Powell took advantage of Hale's having lumped together the separate questions—state entry for geology and the national topographic map. He discussed the first very thoroughly and ignored the idea of a national map, except to say that he had told the appropriations committee of the Senate (Allison and Hale were members) that science in the states would include both geology and topography.[2]

After this initial embarrassment Powell took charge, weakening considerably the feeling against his topographical maps by explaining so well their scientific function. He also assured Congress that the Geological and Coast Surveys were not duplicating each other. When the commission was concerned that a national bureau would swallow state agencies, Powell answered that "the growth of institutions in America is from local centers," and that "the Director . . . has . . . done all within his power to build up State geological surveys." He conveyed valuable information—Chairman Allison was surprised to learn that the maps of the General Land Office did not give true latitude and longitude—and without shocking anybody said that the construction of a geological map in its fullest sense would require 24 years. His success was revealed near the end of the second morning of testimony when the chairman said: "I do not know, Mr. Powell, that we wish to go into much further detail. I have no doubt that you are doing an important work and doing it in a proper way."[3]

---

[2] The citations from the initial dialogue between Powell and the commission are in Record and Hearings of the Joint Commission, 9, 18.
[3] For the quotations in this paragraph, see *ibid.,* 45-46, 165, 177.

When the commission studied the other agencies, Powell became a technical consultant, submitting upon request three lengthy memoranda on maps and methods of constructing them. He also was expansive about plans for unifying the research of the government, criticizing what the National Academy of Sciences had proposed and offering an alternative program. So often and impressively did he testify that he emerged as the dominating figure of the hearings: he talked more about the mapping methods of the Coast Survey than its official representatives. By the end of February 1885 when the commission suspended hearings as Congress adjourned, Powell's prestige in the politico-scientific world had soared. What he had spoken or written seemed important enough to publish. Simon Newcomb reported from Washington that the "Commission has given Powell such a chance as he never had before, and he has improved it. His worst enemy on the Commission can hardly express his high opinion of the straightforward and masterly manner in which Powell handled the problem."[4]

In March 1885 for the first time in 25 years the Democratic party, led by Grover Cleveland, controlled the executive branch of the government. During the election campaign of 1884 Cleveland placed great emphasis on moral issues. He and his party charged corruption in Grant's presidency (1869-1877); they denounced candidate James G. Blaine as spokesman for the lobbyist, spoilsman, and privilege-seeker; and they characterized Republican rule as an era of land grants, subsidies, pensions, and high tariffs. After the inauguration Cleveland wanted to keep his promise to reduce the bureaucracy. Upheavals followed in the Treasury Department, the General Land Office, the U. S. Navy, and public science.

[4] J. W. Powell, *On the Organization of Scientific Work of the General Government* (Washington, 1885). Simon Newcomb to O. C. Marsh, March 7, 1885, Marsh Papers.

Cleveland did not value science as much as his predecessors, Hayes and Garfield. When governor of New York state he entertained, according to topographer Gardiner, "a great and well founded prejudice against the Adirondack Survey, . . . and he is too ignorant to discriminate."[5] Cleveland's reputation of disdain for science followed him to Washington. Stevenson of New York University half expected the new President to send Congress a message denouncing the scientific bureaus as "drain pipes for wasting the people's money."[6] Some months after the change of administrations in Washington Arnold Hague confided his distrust to Becker: "My personal and private belief is that science is not thought highly of at the White House."[7] An early incident must have reinforced Cleveland's low opinion of government science. The first summer he was in office a committee of the Treasury after two weeks of study reported that the condition of the Coast Survey was "one of demoralization" and that its operations had been "inefficient, unjust, and to some degree disreputable."[8] The committee recommended removal of several persons and advised Cleveland to ask for Superintendent J. E. Hilgard's resignation.

Newspaper stories of scandal and corruption began circulating about the Geological Survey. In mid-March the Boston *Daily Advertiser* carried a dispatch from Washington which reported that N. S. Shaler might be Powell's successor. The dispatch said that the Survey had been extravagant and that a change in command would be beneficial.[9] A month later the Cincinnati *Commercial Gazette* charged that members of the Geological Survey were forced to believe in the evolution

[5] J. T. Gardiner to J. W. Powell, December 19, 1883, U. S. Geological Survey, Letters Received, 1883. Gardiner meant the mapping in the Adirondack wilderness by a New York state official, Verplanck Colvin.

[6] J. J. Stevenson to J. W. Powell, November 19, 1884, *ibid.*, 1884.

[7] Arnold Hague to G. F. Becker, December 7, 1885, U. S. Geological Survey, Arnold Hague Letter Books, U. S. National Archives.

[8] New York *Times*, August 7, 1885, p. 3.

[9] Boston *Daily Advertiser*, March 16, 1885, p. 1.

of man from mollusks and baboons. Powell's answer was included in the story. All scientific men accepted some form of evolution; he knew of none who believed what the *Commercial Gazette* said. He also denied that questions of theoretical science or the relation of science to religion influenced the selection of employees, as fitness alone was the criterion. At present two clergymen were employed by the Survey.[10] In June the Boston *Evening Record* repeated the rumor of Powell's retirement; this time Raphael Pumpelly was designated his successor.[11] In late July the unfriendly H. V. N. Boynton of the Cincinnati *Gazette* dug up the controversy about consolidation, saying that the special committee had railroaded its plan through the National Academy of Sciences. While some of the science of the Survey was valuable, Boynton wrote, "much of it is utterly useless, much is trash, much is unreliable, and all of it exceedingly costly."[12]

The climax to these newspaper rumors came after J. Q. Chenoweth, First Auditor of the Treasury, sent three teams of accountants to audit the books of the Survey. In mid-September the New York *Times* reported on its front page that an investigating committee of the Treasury, established by Chenoweth, had discovered three categories of science the Survey had pursued which were not justified by law: the surveys in the eastern states, particularly the topographical mapping in Massachusetts; the examination of mines and mining tracts owned by private individuals; and the research outside the United States. The committee reported that large collections of fossils, instead of being deposited in the National Museum as the law required, were diverted to private museums, notably to those of Professor Marsh of Yale College and Professor Cope of Philadelphia. Also, each year $100,000 went for salaries in excess of the appropriations for specific

10 Cincinnati *Commercial Gazette,* April 13, 1885, p. 2.
11 Boston *Evening Record,* June 4, 1885.
12 Cincinnati *Commercial Gazette,* July 27, 1885, p. 4, and July 31, 1885, p. 5.

jobs. The committee entered a sweeping scientific opinion: much of the Survey's work was "fragmentary" and "valueless."[13]

The newspaper campaign against Powell and the Geological Survey then ceased, perhaps because Auditor Chenoweth declared that there had been no such committee of the Treasury and therefore no investigation, no report, and no illegal proceedings. Simon Newcomb, who knew his way around Washington, blamed the "lying" newspapers. His magazine *Science* lectured the press on truthfulness and said that Chenoweth had grounds for a libel suit. This magazine was particularly irked at the statement, attributed to Chenoweth, that hereafter the Survey must prepare only such materials as the common people would understand.[14]

The report from the accountants, who were a reality, commended Powell and the Survey. After spending three months in the office of J. D. McChesney, King's catch and now Chief Disbursing Clerk of the Survey, these experts concluded everything was in good order. Finally, Chenoweth, having tried his best to break down the finances of the Survey, turned admirer, lauding Powell as "the most laborious public servant he has ever known."[15] Every account, Chenoweth said, was scrutinized by the director before payment.

At the time of the sensational stories in mid-September Powell was not in Washington. Confident of his congressional support, he had gone west on Survey business to return in November. He then took official notice of the unfavorable news by submitting a long letter to Secretary of the Interior L. Q. C. Lamar which listed and appraised all the accusations. He knew of some which have escaped the historian. There were more of the old stories from 1878 and 1879. A "corrupt conspiracy" in the National Academy of Sciences inspired the

[13] New York *Times*, September 16, 1885, p. 1.

[14] *Science*, VI (1885), 261, 301.

[15] N. S. Shaler to Alexander Agassiz, June 27, 1886, Alexander Agassiz Papers, Harvard University.

consolidation; several of the academy scientists "in wicked collusion with Major Powell" planned to erase the lines which traditionally marked the boundaries of all lands sold in the public domain and introduce a new system. Dutton was paid a double salary, one as captain in the U. S. Army and the other as geologist in the Survey. Although on the payroll, Hayden was not active and, in effect, was drawing a pension. The bulletin on geometrid moths lay outside the scope of the Survey. Powell showed a fondness for state geologists, and he paid several of them $4,000 a year. He had bought his way into the National Academy of Sciences "by corruptly distributing patronage." Under his directorship appropriations were obtained by "corrupt lobbying" and large amounts of money "feloniously abstracted from the Treasury."

With denials or a few simple facts Powell dismissed many of the charges. Dutton received no salary as a geologist, and no state scientist ever had drawn any Survey funds. The director could not have used patronage to make his way into the National Academy, for he secured his membership before his appointment as director. The report on geometrid moths had been published by Hayden, not the Survey. The Treasury had never rejected, suspended, or questioned an account of the Survey. He answered the accusation of "corrupt lobbying" with: "No combination of . . . interests has ever been made in order that the Survey might secure an appropriation, and no man, in Congress or out of Congress, has ever been bribed or corruptly rewarded in any manner for his vote or influence; and the patronage of the Survey has never been used for party or political purposes, or to secure legislation."[16]

It would have been better had Powell stopped his disclaimer of corruption short of the topic of patronage, for he distributed it generously at the lower levels of his organization, particularly in the topographic division. Sometimes he had no

---

[16] Powell's comments can be found in J. W. Powell to the Secretary of the Interior, November 5, 1885, U. S. Geological Survey, Letters Sent, 1885.

choice, so insistent were the politicians. More often jobs materialized without summary order. Powell obliged dozens of congressmen, many of them members of appropriation committees. Twice he negotiated compensation, hinging an appointment and a promotion upon congressional approval of money for the Survey. Through patronage he lessened the hostility of the Kentucky delegation, which had plagued King, and he even created a division of forestry to cover the appointment of one broken-down politician.[17]

Nor was Powell completely honest about Hayden, who for years had done little more than submit brief annual reports. Powell told the Secretary of the Interior that Hayden had been busy until 1881 preparing materials for a new volume; thereafter he occupied himself in the office and on the upper Missouri. When the commission learned Hayden had made Philadelphia his headquarters rather than Washington, Powell gave more information but distorted it. "Professor Hayden," he answered, "is something of an invalid; while his mind is as clear and active as at any previous time in his life, by reason of great exposure in making explorations for the Government he is slightly disabled in his lower extremities, so that at the present time it is necessary for him to use crutches. For this reason, he prefers to remain in Philadelphia."[18] Hayden moved from Washington immediately after he was not named director in 1879 and sometime before his illness which, according to memoirs after his death, could not have originated simply in exploring for the government.

The letter to Lamar in November gave some hints as to the source of the stories critical of the Survey. Neither the reporters nor the politicians were so closely connected with science that they could purvey scandal without inside help. Powell's

17 For a period when patronage pressure on Powell was heavy, see U. S. Geological Survey, Letters Received, January, March-July, 1883.

18 J. W. Powell to W. B. Allison, March 24, 1886, U. S. Geological Survey, Letters Sent, 1886.

explanation was that designing persons, disappointed because they did not receive positions in the Survey, had issued the damaging statements. He meant four persons: T. S. Hunt, a chemist and geologist whose official work had been mostly with the Geological Survey of Canada; Persifor Frazer, a member of the Second Geological Survey of Pennsylvania; F. M. Endlich, once with the Hayden survey and now engaged in silver mining; and Cope, the paleontologist. Cope wanted Marsh's job on the Survey.[19] Endlich also longed to join the organization, and he would overthrow Powell to reach his goal. He was active in 1885, interrogating scientists in the hope of uncovering scandalous information and freely predicting the early ruin of the bureau.[20] About Frazer, Powell may have been mistaken. This geologist served very prominently on the American committee of the International Geological Congress and was pressing continually for decisions about classification and nomenclature, which Powell and Gilbert were anxious to avoid. Whether his motivation was mercenary or intellectual, Frazer seemed willing to extend and deepen the differences. In 1890 when the anger of an entire region was directed against Powell because of his irrigation policies, Frazer denounced Powell to Senator W. M. Stewart, leader of the western bloc. Personal feuds were still a factor in the progress of the Survey.

When Congress reconvened in December 1885 the Geological Survey and Cleveland Democracy clashed again, this time at the hearings of the commission and through the challenges of Representative H. A. Herbert of Alabama, one of its members.

Herbert's heartfelt principle was laissez faire, which, along

19 H. F. Osborn, *Cope: Master Naturalist*, 360-61.
20 F. M. Endlich to Henry Gannett, to A. C. Peale, October 13, 1885, in J. W. Powell to the Editor, New York *Herald*, January 12, 1890, p. 11.

with indignation against actual corruption, was an important feature of Cleveland Democracy. Long before his appointment to the joint commission, his faith had been tried and found true. In 1878 he spoke vigorously against a Texas and Pacific railroad bill which would have guaranteed interest payments by the government on $40 million of private bonds. Herbert opposed the bill, although many of his constituents and the legislature of Alabama urged him to support it. He reconciled himself to unpopularity and, therefore, to the possible loss of his seat in the House. But he was reelected, and no doubt he felt vindicated in his views. "I am radically democratic in my views," he told Marsh; "I believe in as little government as possible—that Government should keep hands off and allow the individual fair play. This is the doctrine I learned from Adam Smith & Mill & Buckle, from Jefferson, Benton and Calhoun."[21] Incensed at the expense of peacetime government, a tenfold increase since the days of Jackson, Herbert decided that Congress should eliminate some of the divisions of the Survey or abolish the organization altogether.[22]

He made his bid on December 19, demanding to know the authority for sending Dutton to study volcanoes in the Sandwich Islands. Did not the law of the Survey confine its research to the United States? Why did three bureaus (King's, Wheeler's, and now Powell's) have to publish on the Comstock Lode? Was the bulletin on copper smelting necessary? Would not self-interest publicize this knowledge? Herbert was most effective about Eliot Lord's *Comstock Mining and Miners.* He wanted to know what the history of a mining community had to do with the Geological Survey. Powell made it clear that the volume had been conceived and executed under Clarence King, but Herbert pressed for the director's personal opinion.

21 H. A. Herbert to O. C. Marsh, July 13, 1886, Marsh Papers.
22 H. A. Herbert to Alexander Agassiz, November 27, 1885, Record and Hearings of the Joint Commission, 1013-14.

"You make me do an unpleasant thing in calling upon me to criticize the work of my predecessor," Powell complained.

"But, Major," said Herbert blandly, "I feel like criticizing this work, and want to be supported by the weight of your authority."

"I should not have inaugurated the work," was the reluctant reply.[23]

Taken as a whole, the exchange that December was a stand-off. Powell was ready for the complaint about the Dutton trip: the Smithsonian Institution, not the Geological Survey, had sent him into the Pacific. The director doubted the power of self-interest to make public knowledge out of private discoveries in science or technology. On the contrary, if a person or corporation uncovered something new, they would tend to keep it to themselves for their own moneymaking rather than publish it. Powell cited proprietors of the quicksilver mines in California, who for some time refused to allow Becker access to their properties. In his hostility to science Herbert claimed that the explanation by Ignatius Donnelly of the glacial gravels merited equal consideration with the theory of the geologists. Donnelly, the Populist politician, took a catastrophic view of past change on the earth's surface, writing a book on this earlier and more convulsive history entitled *Ragnorok: The Age of Fire and Gravel*. The event precipitating physical change was the striking of the earth by the tail of a comet with the debris from this tail forming the well-known surface mantle of sand, stone, and gravel. Powell characterized Donnelly's volume as "a kind of geological novel" and told Herbert it bore the same relation to geology as "Jules Verne's romances bear to astronomy."[24]

Herbert could not have been the force he was without the advice of Alexander Agassiz, who believed corruption per-

[23] *Ibid.*, 690.
[24] *Ibid.*, 648.

vaded all government. Agassiz was reluctant to admit that even one scientist in the nation's capital enjoyed a good reputation, as the atmosphere bred politicians. He talked of resigning from the National Academy of Sciences because the members in Washington were too influential. In the summer of 1885 he praised an editorial in the New York *Evening Post* which condemned the American leaders of science for their skill in securing large appropriations.[25] Agassiz would not accept Chenoweth's clean bill of health for the Survey. He thought he knew that hotel bills of visiting foreign scientists were paid out of Survey funds. He apparently influenced Cleveland's decision on the Coast Survey and later was heard to say that Hilgard should have gone to jail. He aided Herbert by identifying possible targets and submitting a letter of criticism for publication. Dutton's journey to Hawaii was illegal. Miners had "learned nothing" from Becker's volume on the Comstock Lode. The man who had helped found the Survey now wrote that its mining geology fell "within the limits of individual investigation." Paleontology was "one of the things which private individuals and learned societies can do just as well as Government. They will do it cheaper." In general the publications of the Survey were "wasteful and extravagant," the topographical division was not called for, and, finally, Agassiz said, "I do not see why men of science should ask more from the government than other branches of knowledge, literature, fine arts, etc."[26]

When Herbert made the letter of Agassiz part of the record of the joint commission, Powell drafted an answer. Every once and a while, ignoring caution and patience, Powell sought to overwhelm an opponent with a torrent of denun-

25 New York *Evening Post*, August 13, 1885. For Agassiz' letter of approval, *ibid.*, September 10, 1885. His letter also appeared in *The Nation*, XLI (1885), 235-36, and in *Science*, VI (1885), 253-54.

26 Alexander Agassiz to H. A. Herbert, December 2, 1885, Record and Hearings of the Joint Commission, 1014-15. H. A. Herbert to Alexander Agassiz, December 3, 11, 1885, Agassiz Papers.

ciation and abuse. He had used this treatment successfully with Hayden in 1879, and now it was Agassiz' turn. In 1890 Cope felt the same stinging pen. Contempt, sarcasm, and anger pervaded the long letter. He complimented his fellow scientist for saying that topography was necessary for geology: "In this statement Mr. Agassiz exhibits a knowledge of the subject matter under consideration not manifest in his other statements, and hence he occupies high ground." But "on that pinnacle of truth" he became "vertiginous" and fell into the error of denying the popular demand for topographical maps. Agassiz' disparaging remarks on the research of the Survey were seen in the harshest light possible. "There is thus published to the American people that a large corps of men, believed by the public to be eminent scholars . . . are but pretenders . . . and the Director . . . the chief of pretenders."

In this letter Powell was an honest collectivist. He who in 1878 had glorified the efforts of individuals now asserted that increasingly in modern civilization solitary research was "futile and inconsequent." But when research formed "an integral part of the operations of some body politic," it steadily became "influential and efficient." The director disputed the Agassiz-Herbert axiom that government was doing research which properly could be left to individuals. If private enterprise was so effective, why had it not accomplished more? The important investigations in western mining, the principal monographs in general geology (with some very few exceptions), and the geological and topographical maps were all published by federal or state governments. Powell had the material in the library of the Survey tabulated to find the ratio of public to private matter and learned that "of the 120,000 pages of general geology taken into consideration not more than about 6,000 are the direct and independent results of private investigation, and of the total information conveyed by the geologic maps enumerated not 5 per cent is the result of independent private investigation." "A hundred millionaires," Powell wrote, "could not do the work in scientific research now done by the General Government; and shall . . . scientific research and the progress of American civilization wait until the contagion of his [Agassiz'] example shall inspire a hundred millionaires to engage in like good works?"

The new Powell rejected the division of labor which confined the government to utilitarian science and left abstract and theoretical research to universities or individual scientists. He had urged this distinction upon the National Academy of Sciences in 1878, and the joint commission had been intrigued with the idea. Now the director was positive about the identity of the scientific and the practical: "knowledge is a boon in itself and in its utilitarian consequences alike," he wrote. Probably he was at his best in calling for all workers, whatever their status, to join in the search for knowledge. The unknown was practically infinite and a wise or generous man (which Agassiz was not) would encourage scientific investigation "in every possible field and by every possible agency." There were "many methods by which the progress of science contributes to the progress of civilization."

Left free to go on and yet not trying to do everything, the Geological Survey could enjoy a busy future, Powell said. The wants of the nation were many and the government agencies to supply them were few. Therefore, the bureau should have "a slow, normal, and healthy growth from year to year until the reasonable demands of the people in all portions of the country now so urgent, shall be met."[27] With this ultimate plea the director closed his long letter of February 26, 1886. He had been the first to testify before the joint commission 15 months before, and now he had the last word in its published hearings.

For two months during the spring of 1886 the future of the Geological Survey was deeply unsettled, as Director Powell

[27] J. W. Powell to W. B. Allison, February 26, 1886, Record and Hearings of the Joint Commission, 1070-84.

sought a firm commitment and Herbert fought noisely to restrict or extinguish the bureau. The resolution of the conflict was effected through the depth and readiness of public and congressional feeling for the Survey, which Powell manipulated to isolate Herbert and his views.

The pace of events accelerated on April 26 when Herbert informed the House he was "instructed by the commission" to submit a bill restricting the work and publications of the Geological Survey.[28] The prohibitions were substantial. The Survey must not discuss "geological theories," and must not publish monographs, bulletins, or any books other than an annual report of transactions.[29] To expedite these prohibitions the Secretary of the Interior was ordered to dispose of laboratories and other Survey property which no longer were needed, and the director was authorized to negotiate with the scientists whose books in progress now would not be published so the authors could make their own arrangements. Finally, the bill asked that in the future estimates and appropriations for printing and engraving be itemized.

Scientists were aroused as they had not been since the days of consolidation. The magazine *Science* characterized the bill as "most disastrous"; should it become law, it would cripple if not entirely destroy the usefulness of the Survey.[30] Newcomb was despondent, saying that Herbert had carried the commission with him. The most outraged person was C. S. Peirce, the founder of pragmatism, who was then doing research for the Coast and Geodetic Survey. He assured Powell of the desire among Coast Survey personnel "to repel this abominable & scandalous attack upon you." Peirce took notice of a rumor that Agassiz had drafted the bill; if true, his conduct was "idi-

28 U. S., *Congressional Record*, 49th Cong., 1st Sess., April 26, 1886, p. 3844.

29 "Restricting the Work and Publications of the Geological Survey, and for other Purposes," U. S., House Report No. 2214, 49th Cong., 1st Sess., p. 1.

30 *Science*, VII (1886), 383.

otic and base." This philosopher called upon scientists to be unphilosophical: "Let the congressmen hear of science, no longer as merely giving reasons, but as an *interest*, saying *We want so and so*." Resolutions should pour into Washington from college faculty members throughout the country; "there are a hundred votes in the house to be commanded in this way," he added.[31]

Some persons were critical of the director, saying he had moved too fast or too confidently. Arnold Hague remembered Powell predicting the commission would not interfere with him. Replying to the warning of Marsh that Herbert intended to abolish the Survey, Representative Hewitt kept his own counsel: "After I have read the bill of Mr. Herbert I shall be able to judge whether he proposes to destroy any legitimate progeny of the system of which you are good enough to say I am the father." There was such a thing as abusing the law; "I do not say that it has been done, but I know very great prejudice has been created in the minds of members of Congress by the character and cost of the publications produced by the Geological Survey." All Hewitt expected was a good geological and topographical map of the United States by a survey like New Jersey's. "I never contemplated the establishment of a scientific publication department for original research." Nevertheless, Hewitt promised to do what he could "to prevent injury to that portion of the work which is really valuable and productive."[32]

Powell's first move was a letter to the commission, published simultaneously in the New York *Tribune* of May 3. It attempted to unhinge that section of Herbert's bill ordering sale of laboratories and other Survey property. The principal properties to be sold under this provision were a portion of the Smithsonian Institution building, a portion of the National

[31] C. S. Peirce to J. W. Powell, May 2, 1886, U. S. Geological Survey, Letters Received, 1886.
[32] A. S. Hewitt to O. C. Marsh, May 3, 1886, Marsh Papers.

Museum building, a portion of the rented Washington building used as Survey headquarters, and a portion of the Peabody
Museum of Yale College. Such a sale was impossible, "and the
provision is nugatory."[33]

Quite right! because within 48 hours (May 5) Herbert told
the House that the joint commission was modifying its bill in
one respect. The section which ordered the Survey to sell other
people's property had been removed. Still seeking the initiative, Herbert said that a written report now accompanied the
substitute bill, and he asked for their printing. He gave the
distinct impression that both the amended bill and the report
were the handiwork of the commission, only to be corrected
tactfully the next day by Allison, who told the Senate he did
not "intend to impute any improper motive." He simply
wanted to say that no report had yet issued from the majority
of the commission, only a bill. Senator J. T. Morgan of Alabama, a Democratic member of the commission since December and cosponsor of the report, made a feeble try at protect-
ing his colleague: "that gentleman [Herbert], who is very careful, has been put in perhaps an improper attitude toward
this matter by some mistake either of the reporters or the
printers."[34]

In his report Herbert tried to show that the real objective
of the Survey was not science at all but self-perpetuation. He
emphasized that after seven years of work no sheets of the
general geological map had yet been published and then cited
Hayden as "an illustration showing that in this Bureau geological monographs sometimes grow to maturity almost as
slowly as geological maps." He tried to give the impression
that the Survey conducted no research in economic geology,
and he scoffed at the publications by giving their market
value. After six years, returns from sales amounted to $1,500,

33 New York *Tribune*, May 3, 1886, p. 5.
34 U. S., *Congressional Record*, 49th Cong., 1st Sess., May 5, 1886, p.
4194; May 6, 1886, p. 4222.

a pittance alongside of the $17 million predicted by him as the ultimate cost of the Survey. The central figure in Herbert's picture of a corrupt Survey was Powell, whom he characterized as the power-hungry director. The representative listed the names and positions of 69 experts (state geologists, professors, editors, engineers, and such) employed by Powell on a per diem basis, mostly for the collection of statistics. Given this large number sustained by the government, could there be "any room . . . for individual enterprise?" "If not," Herbert continued, "then all American geology must be under one man, whose favor must be retained, whose theories must be sustained, and so there can be no independent thought." Herbert and Morgan ended their rhetoric and the report with an "appeal to the best literary and scientific thought of the country to . . . join us in our effort to effect a reform and arrest this pernicious tendency."[35]

The report gained Herbert immediate notoriety, because newspapers began printing stories that Powell employed 69 scientists corruptly. The Cincinnati *Commercial Gazette* published the names of those who "though otherwise regularly engaged, are on the pay rolls of the Survey, some of them receiving as high as $4,000 a year." Here, added the *Gazette*, "are about sixty-nine names of gentlemen apparently located where they will prove most effective."[36]

The more lasting effect of Herbert's sensationalism was to cause a public reaction so strong that Newcomb was soon saying that Powell would "whip the field."[37] J. D. Weeks, who edited trade journals and spoke for the manufacturing interests of Pittsburgh, was one of the accused retainers. In an

[35] "Restricting the Work and Publications of the Geological Survey, and for other Purposes," U. S., House Report No. 2214, 49th Cong., 1st Sess., 6-7, 14-15. Herbert proposed that the Survey model itself after the Geological Survey of the United Kingdom, which, he said, left the discussion of general principles to private individuals, and did not subsidize expensive, sweeping research in paleontology.

[36] Cincinnati *Commercial Gazette*, May 4, 1886, p. 3.

[37] Simon Newcomb to O. C. Marsh, May 10, 1886, Marsh Papers.

interview with a reporter from the Pittsburgh *Leader* Weeks painted an impressive picture of the voluminous correspondence and lengthy reports of Survey statisticians. "It is a labor of love so far as we are concerned," he said. Ordinarily, they were paid $7 to $15 a page for reports and articles. Earnings from the Survey were scarcely enough to cover clerical expenses. Weeks' essay on coke ran to 70 pages and brought him $100. "Strange, is it not," he asked, "that scientific experts should work for the wages of a day laborer, and then be accused of holding a sinecure?" The Geological Survey was "sadly misrepresented"; it had done more to develop the mineral resources of the West than could easily be estimated.[38]

The New Orleans *Times-Democrat,* a paper with a large regional circulation, gave the protest further momentum. "Southerners and those interested in Southern developments are perplexed to account for Herbert's attack on the geological survey," a Washington dispatch began. Herbert represented the Montgomery district of Alabama, and his state and people were "among the greatest beneficiaries of the survey's work," yet here he was proposing a bill which would "utterly destroy the usefulness of the survey." The account focused skillfully on one clause in the bill—the end of publications. The Survey was to go on, but results were not to be published. Herbert proposed to save $100,000 per annum, "and the people will be deprived of information worth millions to them." Herbert wanted this information to become the private property of officials who, having obtained their knowledge at government expense, could then dispose of it for their own profit. "Valuable mines and deposits will be discovered in Alabama, Mississippi, Louisiana or another Southern State, the people's money will have been used to perfect these discoveries, yet the people of the localities themselves will never hear of them. The officers conducting the Survey are proprietors of the in-

38 The Pittsburgh *Leader,* May 6, 1886, as printed in U. S., House Report No. 2740, 49th Cong., 1st Sess., 123. See above, p. 113.

formation, and may sell or speculate upon, or suppress it as they prefer." What Herbert saw in such a bill "to engage his enthusiasm nobody seems able to divine."[39] It was not economy to withhold millions of dollars' worth of information in order to save $100,000, and it was not statesmanship to conduct an important public work so that it fell into the hands of speculators or monopolists. The *Times-Democrat* dispatch ended reassuringly for southern readers. Herbert's opponents were numerous enough to defeat him.

The mounting reaction won Powell another hearing before the joint commission. This late and unscheduled session on May 13 was the freest and frankest in the history of the commission. Almost immediately, there was a skirmish about procedure. Powell had agreed beforehand with Chairman Allison to confine his remarks to the twice-reported bill, the commission's handiwork, and not mention the report by Herbert and Morgan. Accordingly, he handed them his written answer to the report and turned to the bill. Of course Herbert wanted to talk about his report and began quizzing Powell, who answered back. Their exchange irritated Senator Morgan, who resented having to hear criticisms of the report, believing Powell should proceed by communicating with his friends in Congress. Eventually, the committeemen concentrated on what the director had to say. He promised to keep costs of publication for the monographs, bulletins, and maps within a yearly allotment of $80,000, with the public printer paying out of his budget for the annual report and mineral resources volumes. He then lectured on the science of the Survey, stressing the paleontology and laboratory work which the Herbert bill would submerge. After summarizing the rock systems of geological time, locating them geographically, and listing their valuable minerals, Powell explained how these minerals could be exploited more effectively if the systems were identified

39 New Orleans *Times-Democrat,* May 7, 1886, p. 1.

thoroughly. The means of identification were chemical analysis, microscopic study, and examination of fossil remains. His account of Becker's research in cinnabar, the ore of mercury, fascinated Senator Morgan. When Powell described the process by which the ore was concentrated in lodes and beds, the senator exclaimed that the Survey had discovered the "true alchemy." After two hours Morgan, although still supporting Herbert, confessed an error. "I supposed we had gone over all of this. I supposed also there was no practical difference between a paleontologist and a geologist, that they were not two distinct persons; but I find that it takes two men to make a geologist; one is a philosopher, a chemist, and a guide, and the other is a man who does the land work and puts it down on paper." Allison thanked Powell for his very interesting statement.

Despite pledges by Powell that he would bypass Herbert's report, apparently he had planned a calculated outburst against it. About half an hour before the session closed, Herbert rose to go, pleading another engagement. Powell addressed him at once, admitting deep personal feeling over the statement that he "employed sixty-nine gentlemen corruptly," although he knew Herbert did not intend it that way. That was true, Herbert replied, he was casting no stigma on these gentlemen; "I simply thought I ought to put the names of these employes in the report for the reason that they are gentlemen of great social influence—and deservedly—so that when they criticize the report, as they probably will, the world at large will know that they are especial friends and employes of the Geological Survey." The newspapers understood differently, Powell replied, and telegraphed all over the United States that he and 69 honorable gentlemen were accused of crime. "I would like . . . you to telegraph all over the United States what I have stated here," Herbert answered. Powell begged "for justice to these men."[40] Herbert said no more and

40 The committee proceedings are supplied in *The Geological Survey* (Washington, n. d.), 10-33.

departed, but Morgan promised to look into the question and report fairly on it.

Powell and Herbert continued their argument in writing. Powell picked away at the famous list of 69. Three of them were state geologists who received no salary from the federal bureau, and two of them—Marsh and Scudder—were employed regularly by the Survey and nowhere else. Herbert's rejoinders revealed his unwillingness to admit his error even when faced with overwhelming evidence; or if he did, he blamed Powell for his own mistakes. Only once did he rise above the commonplace or the absurd. He was prophetic without wanting to be when he said: "if Congress fails to limit its operations, it is doubtful whether the child is now living who will see the Geological Survey of the United States completed."[41]

The joint commission majority—three Republicans and one Democrat—reported their third and final decision on June 8, and it was a sweeping vindication of Powell and his policies.[42] Twenty years after the western surveys had been inaugurated, the representatives of the people extended the ultimate welcome: "the Commission have no doubt of the wisdom of a geological survey of the whole country, and consider the question of the propriety of its being done by the General Government as settled by existing legislation." The majority agreed with Herbert that over the years the bureau would cost $17 or $18 million, but these four were not shocked as Herbert and Morgan had been. "It is more than probable," they wrote, "that this survey will be continued indefinitely, going on from year to year, with a greater degree of accuracy and refinement

[41] "Limiting the Printing and Engraving for the Geological Survey, the Coast and Geodetic Survey etc.," U. S., House Report No. 2740, 49th Cong., 1st Sess., 112. See also, 109, 115-16.

[42] Senators Allison and Hale, Representatives Robert Lowry of Indiana and J. T. Wait of Connecticut (Lyman's successor in 1885) signed the report. Lowry was the Democrat.

as the population becomes more dense, and as the wealth and resources of the country are developed."[43] Only publishing costs bothered the congressmen. In making their point they favored the figures of the public printer for total government expenditures in lithographing and engraving for the years 1883 to 1885; the Survey had taken one-third of the available monies. The tribute to the efficiency of the Survey was unalloyed, the commission praising Powell for both administrative and business ability. Finally, in an unnecessary abdication of legislative responsibility, the majority refused to shape or judge the configuration of sciences within the Survey. That difficult question should be left to those more intelligent and competent than the commission "with its limited means of knowledge."[44]

Scientists of the Survey rejoiced at this turning point in history. "We all feel very much delighted," wrote Arnold Hague; "the majority report is in every way . . . acceptable to Powell, and I do not see how he could ask for a stronger document." The report was realistic, Hague continued, never dodging or attempting to get around the cost. It said that the work was of national importance and must go on. The

[43] "Limiting the Printing and Engraving for the Geological Survey, the Coast and Geodetic Survey etc.," 51, 53.

[44] *Ibid.*, 52.

The judgment of the Survey's efficiency ignored the effect of the spoils system. Paul Holman, an assistant topographer, was accused of "habitually" absenting himself "from the office for whole days without leave and at other times presents himself for duty at hours ranging between 9 & 11 o'clock; and when late offers no excuse—nor does he show proper interest in his duties when in office." J. H. Renshawe to Henry Gannett, February 7, 1884, U. S. Geological Survey, Letters Received, 1884.

Gannett asked for Holman's resignation through Powell, but the director refused. Surely the delinquent was being protected by his father, W. S. Holman, established Democratic member of the committee on appropriations in the House of Representatives. Later in 1884 the director was told that several employees had done about three days' work all year. They never were in the office, "except on pay days"; and when on hand they passed the time reading, smoking, and sleeping. "A Clerk, USGS" to H. M. Teller, Secretary of the Interior, September, 1884, U. S. Geological Survey, Letters Received, 1884.

doubtful member of the commission had been Robert Lowry
of Indiana; that he had turned out in favor of the Survey
was important, "because he is a Democrat." The most emo-
tional person was Director Powell. Ordering the report read
aloud in his office to listening geologists, he showed "great
glee."[45] Moved to talk about his directorship, he insisted that
he had never gone back on anything which Clarence King
had done; he criticized only King's publishing the *First Annual Report* at his own expense.

Stubbornly, Herbert carried his cause to the floor of the
House. When the appropriation for the Survey was read, without the increase of $100,000 proposed by Powell, the repre-
sentative from Alabama called for an overall reduction of
$35,000 and a ban on the discussion of general principles in
geology and paleontology. Now aiming at the joint commission, Herbert told how the commission, "acting upon the
ideas of Professor Agassiz," framed a bill and authorized him
to report it. But such was the wave of protest from the hundreds of Survey employees, from "the gentlemen of great social
and political influence . . . scattered over the Union," and
from the newspapers which disliked his "audacious attack on
our great Geological Survey," that the majority "repudiated
the bill that had been unanimously reported." This change
of mind showed either cowardice or laziness. Herbert did not
utter these words; he secured their effect by quoting the conversation in *Much Ado about Nothing* between Dogberry and
his watch. Shakespeare's ridiculous character advised his assistants not to bother with vagrants who would not stand "in
the prince's name," nor talk nor babble in the streets, but
preferably to sleep "like an ancient and most quiet watchman." The commission was Dogberry's "ancient and most
quiet watchman," said Herbert. It would not bid Powell

45 This account of feeling within the Survey is based on Arnold Hague
to O. C. Marsh, June 9, 1886, Arnold Hague to Clarence King, June 10,
1886, U. S. Geological Survey, Hague Letter Books.

stand and considered it "most unbecoming to babble in the streets and make a noise about this matter."[46]

The representatives, who earlier in June had three times refused to cut Powell's salary from $6,000 to $4,000,[47] reaffirmed their trust in him. Representative Cannon of Illinois, admitting his ignorance of science, referred to the founding of the bureau seven years before. He remembered "very well ... sitting for an hour and hearing the gentleman from New York advocate its organization as he so ably did. I took what he said upon faith and voted for the organization of this bureau." Powell was a "prudent man," Cannon thought. J. T. Wait of Connecticut, Lyman's successor on the commission, called the director a man of "integrity and sound judgment." When W. M. Springer of Illinois, shocked by Herbert's false statement that scientists fully employed by the Survey were also on private payrolls, submitted an amendment forbidding money of the Survey to any persons privately employed, T. B. Reed of Maine challenged him effectively. Reed entered the dialogue with Springer accepting Herbert's charge as true:

[46] U. S., *Congressional Record*, 49th Cong., 1st Sess., June 29, 1886, pp. 6297-98.

[47] *Ibid.*, June 16, 1886, pp. 5777-78. The Senate also rejected a $1,000 cut in salary by a vote of 34-5. *Ibid.*, July 1, 1886, p. 6395.

There had been a more serious attempt at salary cutting in 1882. The committee on appropriations of the Senate wanted to reduce Powell's salary to $5,000, and those of his six principal assistants (Becker, Emmons, Gilbert, Hague, Hayden, and Marsh) from $4,000 to $3,600, and the Chief Clerk (Pilling) and the Chief Disbursing Clerk (McChesney) from $2,700 to $2,400. Only the salaries of the clerks were actually reduced, and two years later Powell had theirs reinstated by telling Allison that Pilling and McChesney stood between him and two or three hundred other men "to prevent fraud, extravagance, and waste." J. W. Powell to W. B. Allison, June 23, 1884, U. S. Geological Survey, Letters Sent, 1884.

In three sessions with the Secretary and Assistant Secretary of the Interior in the autumn of 1882, Powell successfully fought their suggestion that he go along with the reduction to $3,600 for his six assistants, so as to forestall any further slash. J. W. Powell to O. C. Marsh, October 5, 1882, Marsh Papers. Powell agreed to a vote of the Senate, 34-20, reducing his salary $1,000, but the House never acted. U. S., *Congressional Record*, 47th Cong., 1st Sess., June 28, 1882, pp. 5446, 5448-49.

"REED. What difference does it make how we pay them if we get the equivalent for our money?

"SPRINGER. It makes a great difference if we do not get an equivalent for our money, which I assume to be the fact.

"REED. Precisely. The gentleman from Illinois assumes that to be the fact, but I wish he would give us some evidence of it.

"SPRINGER. I make that assumption, because I assume that if anybody does his duty as a professor in any college in the country he cannot at the same time serve the United States so as to be entitled to a salary.

"REED. But that is entirely an assumption."

There was one moment of excitement for the whole House, and this demonstrated that whatever the strength of the Survey in the East and in the South its devotion to the growth of the West still aroused the most legislative enthusiasm. The discussion had veered to mining geology, and Symes of Colorado was praising Hayden's atlas, the works on the Comstock, the mineral resources volumes, and Emmons' progress at Leadville. Symes had been an attorney for large western mines, and he said these government publications were welcomed by prospectors and superintendents. He also insisted that in this age mining geology should not be confined "to Eastern colleges." Then Wait of Connecticut attracted attention with a few words—something of a surprise since he had been quiet on the joint commission. He appealed to the time-worn theme that America had a destiny to fulfill in the West. Young men who followed Greeley's advice clamored for any information on the public lands. Not to publish this information retarded progress and deterred "the settlement of the Far West and the building up of the splendid towns and cities which in half a century would grow to enrich and brighten and beautify that whole country."[48] Although by no means as lyrical or expansive as Hewitt, Wait evoked applause from the House. The

[48] U.S., *Congressional Record*, 49th Cong., 1st Sess., June 29, 1886, pp. 6299-302.

Survey would get its half million dollars in funds again. Seven years before, the demonstration of support had meant that the Geological Survey would be established. Now, on June 29, 1886, it signified that the bureau was here to stay as a scientific agency of the United States government.

Chapter Eight

YELLOWSTONE PARK: THE GEOLOGICAL
SURVEY AND CONSERVATION

In Yellowstone Park the orientation of the Survey was quite different. Heretofore it had served mineral interests, providing scientific and technical help for the intensive exploitation of natural resources. Its political allies were mining superintendents, engineers, and manufacturers. In the park the Survey stood for the conservation of natural resources, the defense of a recreational area having natural beauty and wonder. It appealed to esthetes, big-game hunters, and urban dwellers tired of the city. The occasion for this change was the coming of the Northern Pacific Railroad to the edge of the park in 1883—and the threat of this coming to the integrity of the region. For a group of promoters and miners sought permission from Congress to extend the railroad into the park, and the Survey moved to oppose the congressional authorization.

Before 1870 government officials were not sure if Americans could ever penetrate the isolated Yellowstone country, but the accelerating westward movement ended this doubt. Now these same officials feared the area would be overrun by business enterprise and technology. Reviving Hayden's old interest in the region, Director Powell established a division of the Yellowstone, placed Arnold Hague in charge, and for 10 years granted him an annual budget of $15,000 to $20,000. Through Hague, the Survey saved the park from invasion and secured a forest reserve in adjacent territory. These two accomplishments, important in themselves, foreshadowed the twentieth

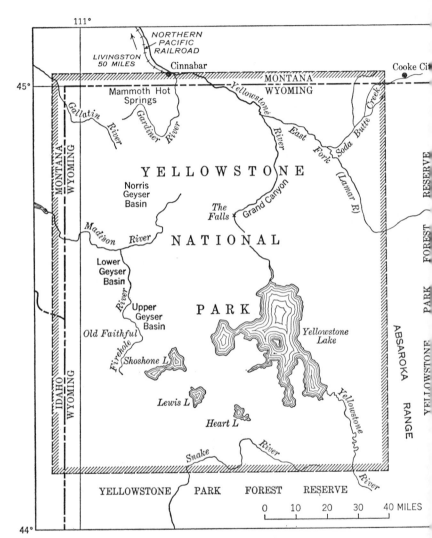

NORTHERN
PACIFIC
RAILROAD

LIVINGSTON
50 MILES

Cinnabar

Cooke City

MONTANA
WYOMING

45°

Mammoth Hot
Springs

Gallatin River

Gardiner River

Yellowstone

River

East Fork

(Lamar R.)

Soda Butte Creek

MONTANA
WYOMING

RESERVE

YELLOWSTONE

Norris
Geyser
Basin

The
Falls

Grand Canyon

Madison River

NATIONAL

FOREST

Lower
Geyser
Basin

River

Upper
Geyser
Basin

PARK

Yellowstone
Lake

PARK

Old Faithful

Firehole

Shoshone L.

Yellowstone

ABSAROKA

RANGE

YELLOWSTONE

Lewis L.

Heart L.

IDAHO
WYOMING

Snake

River

River

YELLOWSTONE   PARK   FOREST   RESERVE

0   10   20   30   40 MILES

44°

YELLOWSTONE PARK IN THE 1890's

century when the American government would establish bureaus of park and forestry service.

The railroad threat to the park materialized in 1884 when a group of promoters in Montana asked permission from Congress to build into the Yellowstone from Cinnabar (now Gardiner), the terminus of the Northern Pacific at the edge of the park. The announced objective was to reach the Clark's Fork mining district at Cooke City, Montana, just outside the Yellowstone at its northeast corner. The projected route lay almost entirely within the park, first running southeast along the Yellowstone River and the East Fork and then heading northeast through Soda Butte Creek to leave the park and reach the mines.

Public opinion in the Montana Territory favored granting the right-of-way. One mine operator, claiming 35 years' experience in California, Utah, and Montana, testified that he never saw so large and promising a mining district as Clark's Fork. Within the area 350 claims had been recorded, 20 or 30 were now being worked, and quantities of the mined ore lay on the ground awaiting transportation to eastern markets.[1] Another operator said that he owned several thousand tons of merchantable ore. Both men said they did not possess a high-grade product, for then it would have been profitable to transport the metal by mule or wagon train. Actually, Cooke City ore consisted of a little silver locked up in a large amount of lead. The expense of transporting the lead by primitive means would have consumed any profit. Let a railroad be built, however, and transportation costs would drop sharply, and 500 tons of ore a week could be moved out of the district. According to the legislature of Montana, "immense quantities of metalliferous ores" were to be found at Cooke City—gold,

[1] C. T. Meader to W. S. Holman, August 13, 1885, U. S., House Report No. 1076, 49th Cong., 1st Sess., 264.

silver, copper, lead, and even coal and iron. "Large numbers of miners" camped there, they said, and "hundreds of thousands of dollars have been invested . . . by capitalists from East and West."[2] Petitions with 500 signatures reached the Senate committee on territories, and the governor of the territory urged passage of the franchise bill. Willing cosponsors in Congress were those hostile to the idea of a government park. Senator J. J. Ingalls of Kansas thought that the government should survey the park and sell it as other public lands were sold. He feared the expense of a corps of officials "to look after the spouting geysers, to see that patent medicines are not advertized on the cliffs; that timber is not cut down, and that the noble game is not excluded from those preserves." Ingalls thought that private enterprise would protect the natural curiosities.[3]

The challenge by the railroad led friends of the park to reinterpret its purpose. They began emphasizing the park's untamed and unspoiled condition, ranking this feature with the geological wonders whose protection had inspired the founders in 1872. Secretary of the Interior Lamar, writing to the Senate in 1886, said that the Yellowstone was a "rugged, romantic, beautiful wilderness and wonderland," which preserved "for the benefit of those who shall come after us something of the original 'Wild West.' "[4] W. H. Phillips, a Washington lawyer and Hague's associate in Yellowstone affairs, glorified the idea of inviolability. For persons bound by "the trammels of civilized life," the "main joy and wonder" of the park was its natural beauty; "the fair picture contained no blot of man's hand." Now, continued Phillips, "the face of nature is to be seared . . . and one of the fairest portions of

2 Memorial of the Legislature of the Territory of Montana, U. S., Senate Misc. Doc. No. 9, 48th Cong., 1st Sess., 1.

3 U. S., *Congressional Record,* 47th Cong., 2nd Sess., March 1, 1883, p. 3488.

4 L. Q. C. Lamar to C. F. Manderson, April 22, 1886, U. S., House Report No. 1386, 53rd Cong., 2nd Sess., 3-4, 8.

the park surrendered to a corporation" with authority in the language of the bill to erect "station houses, depots, and machine shops."[5]

Hague was himself a convert to the idea of the park as a wilderness area, but he had an economic rather than a recreational reason for doing so. He wanted the park for use as a water and forest reserve. He argued that the Yellowstone country's climate made it an oasis in the Rocky Mountain region. Although possessing few statistics, he believed the precipitation was above average—heavy snow in the winter and frequent rain during the summer. How else could one explain the sizable bodies of water—Yellowstone, Shoshone, Lewis, and Heart Lakes—the hundreds of thermal and cold springs, and, "in striking contrast with the greater part of the Rocky Mountains," the numerous ponds, marshes, and meadows?[6] The quantity of water leaving this mountain reservoir through Yellowstone, Snake, and other drainage systems was the equivalent of a river five feet deep and 190 feet wide, and it flowed at the rate of three miles an hour. This resource should go to the arid plains of the lower Yellowstone Valley or to land farther down on the Snake River. The forests, which covered 80 percent of the ground in pine, balsam, and fir, helped regulate the water runoff, so that the lower valleys would be spared disastrous floods.

To involve the Yellowstone in the conservation of natural resources, Hague submitted a bill to Congress enlarging the park by incorporating other timberland which also belonged to the Yellowstone or Snake watersheds. He proposed adding a strip 25 miles wide on the east and a smaller piece 10 miles deep on the south. The first was the Absaroka Range, which Hague called the roughest country in the Rocky Mountains and the barrier which delayed for so long the discovery of

[5] W. H. Phillips to the Secretary of the Interior, April 6, 1886, *ibid.*, 6.
[6] "The Yellowstone Park as a Forest Reservation," *The Nation*, XLVI (1888), 9.

the park. From northeast-moving winds this range drew moisture, which entered the park as mountain torrents or flowed east into the Big Horn River, a lower branch of the Yellowstone. The characteristic tree was the tamarack or black pine, which in Montana and Wyoming supplied railroad ties and satisfied charcoal burners. The 10-mile strip to the south of the park was less rugged but equally mountainous. It made almost ideal timberland and collected water for the south-flowing Snake River.

The proposed enlargement of the park gave Hague another argument for keeping it in a state of nature—let it be a preserve for big game now facing extermination on the continent. He discounted the original area of the park as game country. The north and south line of the hot springs and geyser basins had never been inhabited heavily by the larger wild animals, and the extensive volcanic plateau, forming the main floor of the park, offered only limited grazing opportunities. Good breeding ground for deer, however, lay immediately south, and the Absaroka Range to the east supported bighorn or mountain sheep, which were prized by hunters. Hague hoped that the antelope, the moose, the elk, and the buffalo would also make the upper Yellowstone country their refuge.[7]

The railroad interest made real progress in the spring of 1886 when the Senate committee on railroads and the House committee on public lands reported favorably on a right-of-way through the park to Cooke City. Legislative tactics were menacing and abusive. Friends of the park were told "time and again" that if they refused the railroad bill, "not a dollar" would go for the protection of the park, and that ultimately the act of incorporation would be repealed.[8] Senator G. G. Vest of Missouri, an eloquent advocate of the Yellowstone,

[7] The Yellowstone Park as a Game Reservation, manuscript, U. S. Geological Survey, Hague Letter Books.

[8] U.S., *Congressional Record*, 49th Cong., 1st Sess., August 2, 1886, p. 7844.

knew that "when any public man stands in the way of one of these speculative enterprises the first thing is to cajole him or buy him, and if that can not be done the next thing is to destroy him."[9] Promoters and politicians turned the power of the Northern Pacific Railroad against the defenders of the park. This railroad carried practically all traffic out to and back from the civilized world, and through a subsidiary, the Yellowstone Park Association, owned hotels or camps at all the centers of attraction—Mammoth Hot Springs, Norris Geyser Basin, the Lower and Upper Geyser Basins, Yellowstone Lake, and the Grand Canyon. First secretly and then openly the association controlled the park's largest stagecoach company, which operated into the Yellowstone from the railroad station at Cinnabar. Unquestionably, the subsidiary had monopolistic aims, because it made things difficult for G. L. Henderson, the independent proprietor of a transportation firm doing one-third of the business in the park, and the manager of a hotel at Mammoth Hot Springs, owned by two other members of the Henderson family. Henderson complained that he was forbidden to solicit passengers at the hotels of the association, and that "the stages of the Park Association were allowed good places," at Cinnabar station, while competing teams were driven away.[10] A brother, D. B. Henderson, who sat in the House of Representatives from Iowa and later became Speaker, reported that the manager of the association's hotel at Mammoth Hot Springs "insults every laboring man who appears on the threshold of this hotel." Henceforth, anyone who spoke in favor of the park was called a tool of the Northern Pacific and a friend of monopoly. P. B. Plumb, senator from Kansas, erroneously contended that all the hotels and stages were controlled by one organization. And Representative J. H. Reagan hoped that "the time will come, and

9 *Ibid.*, June 21, 1886, p. 5947.
10 Arnold Hague to Moses Harris, May 22, 1888, U. S. Geological Survey, Hague Letter Books.

that as early as possible, when that park will be abandoned,"
because "as long as it lasts it will be a source of corruption,
jobbery, and scandal."[11]

The forces favoring the park examined critically the franchise venture. Hague twice visited the Clark's Fork mining
district at Cooke City. Knowing that the number of mining
claims had often very little to do with the importance of a district, he made "careful inquiry" and learned that only 100 miners actually were at work, and all the diggings were shallow and
never occupied by more than three or four men. Hague came
away convinced that exaggerated stories were being circulated
about this small and undeveloped district, and he refused to
believe that a $1 million railroad was financially justified.
Senator Benjamin Harrison of Indiana doubted that the railroad would ever be built solely to carry ore from Clark's Fork,
but rather it was designed for tourist travel.[12] Vest argued that
the franchise was only the first move in opening the Yellowstone to general exploitation: "The idea is to get into the park,
and then when the main line is constructed up the Yellowstone River it follows as a corollary, as a logical sequence, that
branches were to be constructed and run down to the geysers,
to the Yellowstone Lake, and to the falls of the Yellowstone."
Last year a bill had been introduced for a Green River branch
of the Union Pacific, coming up from the south, past Lewis
Lake (within the park) to Cinnabar on the northern boundary. Now held in abeyance, it would be immediately urged
by "this other set of speculators," should the pending legislation pass. Vest threatened to capitulate if even one railroad
were allowed: "I for one will vote to throw the whole park

11 U. S., *Congressional Record,* 49th Cong., 1st Sess., August 2, 1886,
pp. 7865-66.

Hague found Henderson, the congressman, "wild and beyond all
reason." Arnold Hague to G. B. Grinnell, February 12, 1889, U. S. Geological Survey, Hague Letter Books.

This trouble disappeared in 1889 when the Henderson family sold out
to the association, and the brother in the park became its employee.
Arnold Hague to G. B. Grinnell, February 16, 1889, *ibid.*

12 U. S., *Congressional Record,* 48th Cong., 1st Sess., May 27, 1884, p. 4551.

into the public domain and let the first and fastest man enter
Old Faithful for laundry purposes and take the great falls of
the Yellowstone for a mill."[13] Others believed that a franchise
was attractive, because it might be sold to the leading conces-
sionaire, the Northern Pacific Railroad.

The Forty-ninth Congress listened to both sides during its
first session and took no action. But just before adjournment
on August 2, 1886, the House of Representatives eliminated
the annual appropriation for the Yellowstone, leaving the
park without a superintendent and compelling the Secretary
of the Interior to have the U. S. Army police the area. In the
bitterness of defeat Hague asked who was going to protect
Yellowstone against its protectors. "Of all people I have ever
seen in the Park for defacing the formation the United States
soldier takes the cake," he wrote.[14] Afterward, he was more
philosophical, admitting to an army lieutenant that the park
could be well served under either the Department of the
Interior or the War Department. The paramount recommendation of the military was that only the soldier with a gun
could curb the lawless skin hunter. The army officer also
proved himself more immune to collateral moneymaking ventures which cursed so many civilian officials. On the other
hand, the War Department was not organized to maintain
a national park. No sooner had a good man learned the job
than he was likely to be transferred elsewhere.

When the Forty-ninth Congress reconvened in December
1886 the park's proponents rallied in the House against the
railroad bill. Hague's fresh ideas had their effect. Representative Cannon said it was "far more important to preserve
the timber . . . to feed these streams . . . for the purpose of
irrigation along their borders, than to open up this mining
camp." W. S. Holman, a Democrat, also favored the forest

13 U. S., *Congressional Record*, 49th Cong., 1st Sess., June 21, 1886,
p. 5949.
14 Arnold Hague to D. W. Wear, August 10, 1886, U. S. Geological
Survey, Hague Letter Books.

idea, fearing floods.[15] On December 14, the day of debate, S. S. Cox of New York made a speech rhapsodizing about the sublime in nature without arousing congressional prejudice against such themes. When, the previous June, M. C. Butler of South Carolina had said that he could not sympathize with the "esthetic view of the Park," Vest had replied quickly that he was "past that word 'esthetic.' "[16] Vest had expounded the theme of a patriotic experience—the nation loved its "republican park . . . a great breathing-place for the national lungs," where people could go, instead of to the Alps for the wonders of nature, or to the Orient.[17] Representative Cox used this patriotic argument as protective coloration for the esthetic appeal, saying Yellowstone Park had great beauty and was a marvelous and rare possession of the American people, who were only performing their "national duty" in preserving it. He defined the opposing forces as "corporate greed and natural selfishness against national pride and natural beauty." He said the question could not be decided by a few people interested in a mining venture. "It is a question for the United States, and for all that gives elevation and grace to our human nature, by the observation of the works of physical nature." And when he ended with the words, "let us vote it down and preserve this marvelous scenery for our people to-day, and for our posterity," applause broke out.[18] A few minutes later, Cox moved that the enacting words of the railroad bill be struck out, and the House supported him, 107 to 65. At least for the Forty-ninth session of Congress the scheme was dead. With manifest relief Hague spread the good news.[19]

15 U. S., *Congressional Record*, 49th Cong., 2nd Sess., December 14, 1886, pp. 151, 154.

16 U. S., *Congressional Record*, 49th Cong., 1st Sess., June 21, 1886, p. 5949.

17 U. S., *Congressional Record*, 47th Cong., 2nd Sess., March 1, 1883, p. 3488.

18 Cox's speech is given in U.S., *Congressional Record*, 49th Cong., 2nd Sess., December 14, 1886, pp. 150-51.

19 Arnold Hague to G. B. Grinnell, December 21, 1886, to Edward Hofer, December 21, 1886, U. S. Geological Survey, Hague Letter Books.

A stalemate followed the climactic events of 1886. Four years in a row (1887-1890) the Senate approved the bill expanding the park and strengthening its government, but each year the House rejected it. There the railroad element, which after the engagement in 1886 despaired of ever winning a franchise through independent legislation, twice persuaded the committee on the public lands to amend the senatorial bill to add what they wanted. But on the floor of the House their congressional sympathizers could not overcome, either by stealth or by persuasion, the objections of the park enthusiasts, who were unable to remove the obnoxious amendment and proceed without it.[20]

Hague and his allies worked hard to arouse public opinion, and they were moderately successful. The antimaterialists, who rejected urban civilization, came to the defense of the park's pristine condition. Their most articulate spokesmen were two magazine editors, C. S. Sargent of *Garden and Forest* and G. B. Grinnell of *Forest and Stream*. "A great natural possession," Sargent wrote, had "peculiar power . . . to calm the fevered unrest of overcrowded, hurried modern life; to delight and reinvigorate all who feel that 'the world is too much with us, late and soon.' " Sargent saw parks and forests as bringing out the "ideal element in our nature," which was the source of poetry, romance, and art.[21] The major New York newspapers supported the park bill.

Hague's game preserve idea evoked considerable response from sportsmen. In 1888, 20,000 persons, principally from gun clubs and sporting associations, petitioned Congress to pass the bill of enlargement. The campaign was engineered by the Boone and Crockett Club of New York City, a group of eastern,

[20] In the last days of the Fifty-first Congress, first session, the park bill with the franchise as an amendment was presented and might have passed had not Speaker Reed said, "this bill is liable to provoke discussion, is it not?" U. S., *Congressional Record*, 51st Cong., 1st Sess., September 29, 1890, p. 10696.

[21] *Garden and Forest*, II (1889), 505, 529. Mr. Bart Hague of New Haven, Connecticut, told me of this quotation.

wealthy persons who hunted big game. Theodore Roosevelt was a charter member, its first president, and a faithful attendant at the annual banquet. Hague and Phillips also were members. This club printed petition forms and mailed them to groups in the Northeast and the Ohio Valley. Senator J. R. Hawley of Connecticut returned the petition from New Britain with the signatures of Judge V. B. Chamberlain and 51 other residents; "they are," Hawley said, "gentlemen of character and intelligence, and, if that is of any use, they are men of wealth."[22] Senator Plumb, who often had given the impression that he wished the park abolished, acknowledged the force represented by these petitions, for after they were submitted, he assured the Senate that he believed in Yellowstone.[23]

Despite these developments, legislators in both friendly and hostile circles doubted the park was popular. "Outside of those of us who are aesthetic and sentimental, as we are told in regard to this reservation," confessed Senator Vest, "there seem to be very few persons who care anything" about it.[24] He realized that only a few thousand visited the park annually, and he blamed this on the acquisitive spirit, which sacrificed to moneymaking "all esthetic taste and . . . all love of nature and its great mysteries and wonders."[25] He might equally have cited the cost of a visit by rail, which was several hundred dollars, far beyond the reach of average Americans. The lack of popularity of the park was a favorite point with its critics. Answering Vest, Senator Butler congratulated his colleague for having "hunted in that great park of the West, and fished in its streams and enjoyed its magnificent scenery. I have never had that opportunity, and . . . very few of my

22 U. S., *Congressional Record,* 50th Cong., 1st Sess., April 17, 1888, p. 3030.

23 *Ibid.,* April 10, 1888, p. 2825.

24 U. S., *Congressional Record,* 52nd Cong., 1st Sess., May 10, 1892, p. 4121.

25 U. S., *Congressional Record,* 47th Cong., 2nd Sess., March 1, 1883, p. 3488.

constituents will ever have that opportunity."[26] Senator J. H. Berry of Arkansas claimed that the raising of wild animals would benefit only a few wealthy individuals. Berry thought the way to make the park serve democracy would be to sell it to the highest bidder, "and I would turn that money into the Treasury of the United States to belong to the whole people."[27]

Hague's morale suffered as he saw his hopes fade for the popularity of the park. Urged by Senator C. F. Manderson of Nebraska "to create a favorable sentiment" by personal interviewing in the House, he murmured that this was "laborious work" and "a great consumer of time."[28] When in 1887 Congress again denied an appropriation for a civilian superintendent, he denounced one of the representatives on the conference committee. "Ryan comes from Kansas," he said, "where they have no trees, and he fails to appreciate the beauty of anything but corn and hogs."[29] In 1888 he complained to Grinnell of *Forest and Stream* that "there is an end to one's patience and zeal."[30] He dreaded attacks by Plumb and Ingalls, and he overheard a remark by Vest that Yellowstone was more trouble than the tariff. In 1890 when the park and railroad groups fought each other to a standstill for the fourth time, with the Senate passing the boundary bill and the House amending it for a right-of-way, Hague thought it was small comfort "after long years of work" merely "to defeat an objectionable measure."[31] Early in 1891, the same gloomy tone reached Sargent of *Garden and Forest*.[32]

Suddenly at the nadir of his feelings Hague saw a way to

[26] U. S., *Congressional Record*, 49th Cong., 1st Sess., June 21, 1886, p. 5949.

[27] U. S., *Congressional Record*, 52nd Cong., 1st Sess., May 10, 1892, p. 4125.

[28] Arnold Hague to G. B. Grinnell, December 20, 1886, U. S. Geological Survey, Hague Letter Books.

[29] *Ibid.*, March 4, 1887.

[30] *Ibid.*, September 6, 1888.

[31] Arnold Hague to J. N. Brown, December 19, 1890, *ibid.*

[32] Arnold Hague to C. S. Sargent, March 5, 1891, *ibid.*

secure the withdrawal from the public domain of the accessory land without a popular uprising and without congressional consent. The Fifty-first Congress gave him his opportunity. At the very end of the session this Congress overhauled the legislation on the public lands, amending the homestead and desert land acts and repealing the preemption and timber culture laws. These changes, all incorporated in the Act of March 3, 1891, had been discussed publicly for years. The final section, designated number 24 and added in conference committee at the urging of the American Association for the Advancement of Science, authorized the President to establish forest reservations in the public domain. Half a century later Gifford Pinchot called Section 24, "the beginning and basis of our whole National Forest system."[33] If the 25-mile zone to the east and the 10-mile belt to the south could not be added to the original park, would not the setting aside of this land as a public forest reservation under the Act of March 3 accomplish the same result?

Hague negotiated with Secretary of the Interior Noble and President Harrison. Secretary Noble, who had coaxed the forest reserve clause from a reluctant conference committee, was very receptive. He asked Hague to prepare a statement defining boundaries and a letter justifying withdrawal. "We hope," Hague advised a friend, "to get the land set aside without any newspaper discussion until the thing is accomplished."[34] The Secretary relayed Hague's statement and letter to President Harrison, together with a map showing the boundaries of the reservation. Harrison needed little persuading; while in the Senate he had been one of the outspoken defenders of the park, probably because he had once visited there and, like everyone else, had come back all aglow over the wonders and scenery. On March 30, 1891, he issued the proclamation which

33 Gifford Pinchot, *Breaking New Ground* (New York, 1947), 85.
34 Arnold Hague to J. N. Brown, March 16, 1891, U. S. Geological Survey, Hague Letter Books.

established the first forest reserve and located it on the eastern and southern margins of Yellowstone Park.[35]

Hague told an army officer detailed to the Yellowstone country that he felt "very happy over the proclamation of the President setting apart the new timber reservation . . . it adds eight and one-half miles to the south and between 24 and 25 miles to the east, in all over 15 hundred square miles."[36] A letter to Clarence King carried this statement: "I think I may be congratulated on getting this thing through."[37] He informed Sargent that "I . . . have already received a good many congratulations upon my success in at last getting it set aside after so many years of toil in trying to have it attached to the Park."[38] And he read with pleasure in *Forest and Stream* that "Mr. Arnold Hague, of the United States Geological Survey, whose intimate knowledge of the Park extends back over a number of years, has long been a consistent worker for this reservation."[39]

In 1892 the railroad interest tried once again to seek approval to enter the park, precipitating the final legislative clash. This time there was a serious attempt to reach a compromise. Persons on both sides united and urged restoration to the public domain of the area above the Yellowstone River and its East Fork in the northeast corner of the park. Congress could then grant the right-of-way without violating the park or even diminishing it much in size. Powell, Hague, and Noble approved the plan, and the park advocates in the Senate—Vest, Manderson, and Dawes—agreed that it was the best solution. The miners at Cooke City sent a committee to advocate the northeast cutoff, as it came to be called; favor-

[35] "Proclamations of the President of the United States," U. S., *Statutes at Large*, XXVI (1889-1891), No. 17; XXVII (Washington, 1891-1893), No. 6.
[36] Arnold Hague to John Pitcher, April 7, 1891, U. S. Geological Survey, Hague Letter Books.
[37] Arnold Hague to Clarence King, April 4, 1891, *ibid*.
[38] Arnold Hague to C. S. Sargent, April 7, 1891, *ibid*.
[39] "A New Forest Reserve," *Forest and Stream*, XXXVI (1891), 225.

able petitions were submitted from Miles City, the Helena Commercial Club, the Board of Trade of Bozeman, and the city council at Butte.

The compromise measure was fatal to those forces opposing the park which had pretended to campaign for a railroad to Cooke City when actually they wanted a franchise within the park. This faction used the Montana Mineral Railway Company, successor to the defunct Cinnabar and Clark's Fork corporation; financial backing was reported to be available through Mayor E. H. Fitler of Philadelphia. For a time the group's lobbyist in Washington was Daniel May, a citizen of Billings, Montana, and beef contractor for the park. Backers of this "railway company" persuaded the House committee on public lands to vote six to four for the right-of-way through the park. During the discussion the lawyer for the company said the compromise proposal was wicked, and he hinted that anyone favoring it must be connected with the Northern Pacific Railroad.[40] After the public break with the Cooke City miners, the Montana Mineral Railway Company was attacked so effectively that it ceased to have any practical function. In the Senate W. F. Sanders of Montana declared that the citizens of Montana repudiated the company, which had never actually existed, he said.[41] T. F. Oakes, president of the Northern Pacific, confirmed the common rumor that the Montana company had been offered for sale. A man named Rickey residing at Willard's Hotel had told Oakes that the Mineral road would sell for $12,000, if it secured the right-of-way.[42]

The Cooke City miners were no more successful in getting the northeast corner of the park segregated. President Oakes was authoritative here: "We had a report upon . . . [the mines] by experts. There is a very large deposit of exceedingly low-

[40] "Report from the Committee on the Public Lands—Montana Mineral Railway Company," U.S., House Report No. 854, 52nd Cong., 1st Sess., 4.
[41] U.S., *Congressional Record*, 52nd Cong., 1st Sess., May 10, 1892, p. 4123.
[42] "Inquiry into the Management and Control of the Yellowstone National Park," U. S., House Report No. 1956, 52nd Cong., 1st Sess., 226.

grade ore. The maximum would not exceed $20 to the ton, and most of it would not be over $6 to the ton. If there had been one-tenth of the deposit and the ore had a value of $50 or $60 a ton we would have made an effort to get a railroad in there, but there is nothing there for a railroad. That is my judgment."[43] Nothing has since happened to question Oakes' conclusion, and no railroad has ever been built. The trouble caused by the few promoters of an inferior mining district suggests the consequences for the park if real economic wealth had been discovered there. Almost certainly the railroad would have penetrated the area. Years before, Hayden sensibly had pleaded the poverty of the Yellowstone country in agricultural and mineral resources. Before strong legislation this lack of resources was the park's greatest asset without which the friends of the park would have been helpless.

In 1894 the Yellowstone period of the history of the Survey was achieved. That year Congress with little debate passed two bills which friends of the park had been urging for years. The Lacy Act established the jurisdiction of federal courts and broadened the powers of the Secretary of the Interior. The Hayes Act strengthened the Secretary's position in dealing with the troublesome leasing system. These two acts, together with the forest reserve to the east and south, made it unlikely that Yellowstone would ever be overrun by speculative enterprise. The need for a leader such as Arnold Hague to police the area and lobby aggressively on Capitol Hill disappeared, but the bureau's activity in forestry affairs did not cease. When Hague moved so swiftly to make the first reserve under the Act of 1891, he undoubtedly prepared the way for what happened later in the decade. At that time (1897) the Geological Survey was designated the agency to study and map the forest reserves established by Grover Cleveland. From this vantage point the Survey guided the forces of conservation into the Progressive Era of the early twentieth century.

[43] *Ibid.*

Chapter Nine

THE IRRIGATION SURVEY:
SCIENCE AND REFORM

In 1888 when western sentiment was ready Powell directed the Geological Survey into the study of irrigation. He still sought to combine science and reform. If the research of the Survey previously had served private individuals or corporations, now Powell wanted it to help people form communities to own and control all the lands of the arid region. This time he did not have to consult with other scientists, and even Congress was not disposed to challenge him, as the legislators were interested primarily in the implications of his plan for the public land system. The history of the Geological Survey was affected deeply by Powell's desire to direct the course of western settlement through scientific knowledge. For two years the study of irrigation dominated the activities of the Survey. Then congressional hostility forced the abandonment of the project. The Survey became the most unpopular bureau of the federal government, and Powell lost the directorship.

By 1888 public opinion in favor of irrigation in the states and territories beyond the one hundredth meridian was strong enough to draw government response. For various reasons many westerners felt that if economic progress were to continue in their communities, then irrigation based on reservoir storage must be developed. A declining rainfall with consequent loss of stream water dramatized the need for action in Colorado. The problem in Utah was the increased demand for water, which threatened the supply available without reservoirs. Annoyed at the poor silver market, Nevada citizens also began thinking about large irrigation enterprises, while in Arizona many people were anxious to exploit the unused potential of the Gila and Salt Rivers. Most of these places wanted to attract private capital, and they hoped the federal government would collect information about irrigation for the benefit of potential investors.

Senators H. M. Teller of Colorado and W. M. Stewart of Nevada initiated formal political action in February and March 1888. Teller introduced a resolution passed by the House and the Senate which outlined the primary information expected by Congress from a scientific survey.[1] This resolution ordered the Geological Survey to investigate reservoir building for water storage in arid regions. Two other directives were initiated by Stewart through two resolutions approved by the Senate alone.[2] Stewart's resolutions asked that the Geological Survey distinguish the public lands capable of irrigation, lay out rights-of-way for ditches and canals, and make maps of the valuable sites and areas.

Through his replies to these resolutions and during the subsequent negotiations Powell reached the climax of his influence as a public administrator. He who once had been so diffident compared to Hayden or King now directed an organization which dominated American research in geology and paleontology and also operated as a bureau of mines. He was making a national map and had founded a park and forestry service. He still retained the directorship of the Bureau of Ethnology. And in 1888 he was the only outsider who seemed to count with Congress as it moved slowly toward authorizing an irrigation survey. To bring the Teller and Stewart resolutions into the legislative process he drafted a bill which read as follows: "For the purpose of investigating the ex-

---

[1] U. S., *Statutes at Large,* XXV (Washington, 1887-1889), 618-19.
[2] U. S., *Congressional Record,* 50th Cong., 1st Sess., February 11, 1888, p. 1137; March 27, 1888, pp. 2428-29.

tent to which the arid region of the United States can
be redeemed by irrigation, and the segregation of the irrigable
lands in such arid region, and for the selection of sites for
reservoirs and other hydraulic works necessary for the storage
and utilization of water for irrigation, and to make the necessary maps . . . the work to be performed by the Geological
Survey . . . the sum of two hundred and fifty thousand
dollars."[3]

Then he appeared before the Senate committee on appropriations to explain what the field science would be if the
bill passed. The committee learned he planned to map drainage districts for six years, making topography "the essential
thing" and "chief cost."[4] Powell had said in 1884 that topographical mapping was the most useful science in which the
government could be involved, and he had begun the national map. The irrigation survey meant the opportunity to
quicken the pace of this mapping in the West.

Powell's advocacy of the bill, combined with his prestige,
gave the irrigation bill its initial momentum. Chairman Allison of the committee on appropriations found him "able and
strong and plausible, as he always is, as to the enormous
benefits that would result from authorizing him to enter upon
this survey."[5] When Stewart was accused of planning government construction of reservoirs and canals, he was glad to
have Powell and the Geological Survey as proof that nothing
so radical was intended. "Eighty per cent of the proposed
work," said the senator, "is topography, the same work in
which the bureau is now engaged . . . it is of the same character precisely." He praised Powell as "competent, energetic,
and enthusiastic." Senator D. W. Voorhees of Indiana thought

[3] J. W. Powell to the Secretary of the Interior, May 3, 1888, U.S.G.S.
Tenth Annual Report, Part II, *Irrigation,* 14.

[4] U. S., Senate Report No. 1814, 50th Cong., 1st Sess., 119. He estimated
total costs as $5 million and duration of the survey as six years.

[5] U. S., *Congressional Record,* 51st Cong., 1st Sess., August 26, 1892, p.
9149.

the director "one of the most useful and scientific men of his age, and he will be remembered by his glorious works long after the rest of us are forgotten."[6] For Marcus Smith, the territorial representative from Arizona, Powell stood "like the shadow of a great rock in a weary land."[7]

The natural place for the managers of the bill in the Senate to begin their campaign was with the committee on the public lands, but P. B. Plumb, the chairman, declined to cooperate, calling all favorable arguments "trash." If the West were settled now, he went on, there would be no open land in the future for people from the crowded cities. To this inane statement he added sharp words against Powell and his bureau, who were, he contended, the real force behind the irrigation movement. "The Geological Survey is the lying-in hospital of the Government," he charged. "It never yet refused employment to a single relative of a Congressman or to any one who is supposed to be influential in regard to obtaining appropriations." The Survey had been the "worst expenditure" of funds since the beginning of the government. If it were not for Powell's hope of spending money, the bill would not have the headway to wash "a handful of earth in the Arkansas valley." Powell wanted another job so that Congress could hear all about it "on the finest letter-press"; the only visible result would be cartloads of books and pictures. Finally, "he expects some day to be incorporated into the Constitution of the United States as an amendment."[8]

Plumb and his committee were bypassed through maneuvers on the floor of the Senate. On May 14 Senator Stewart informed his colleagues that the Powell bill had arrived from the Department of the Interior, and he moved that it be referred to the committee on appropriations. When two other

[6] U. S., *Congressional Record*, 50th Cong., 1st Sess., July 30, 1888, pp. 7015, 7022, 7024.
[7] *Ibid.*, September 10, 1888, p. 8477.
[8] *Ibid.*, July 30, 1888, pp. 7021, 7023.

senators proposed the committee on agriculture and forestry,
Stewart switched to the committee on the public lands. No
more was heard from this committee, and later several of its
members denied any knowledge of the bill. On the same day
A. S. Paddock of Nebraska, chairman of the committee on
improvement of the Mississippi River, reported an appropriation for the Geological Survey to study irrigation. Senator
Paddock identified his recommendation as an amendment to
the river and harbor appropriations bill, submitted a few days
before by Senator T. M. Bowen of Colorado. This Bowen
amendment was the Powell bill with a six-word insertion,
"the prevention of floods and overflows." Upon Stewart's motion the Powell or Bowen amendment was referred to the
committee on appropriations.[9]

This committee refused to authorize money for an irrigation
survey, fearing that it committed the government to more
than collection of information. It was one thing, said Eugene
Hale of Maine, simply to locate reservoirs and quite another
if "a system of . . . reservoirs and canals" at government
expense was going to develop out of the fact finding. Stewart,
of course, was sure that private enterprise would take hold
of the streams, once the government had found the reservoir
sites, the canal lines, and the irrigable lands. Local promoters
would succeed; he had seen miners in California make their
own regulations about water. He boasted that "our people
can manage the system better than even" the people of Spain
or India "because they are more intelligent."[10] Chairman
Allison was not impressed. He thought that sooner or later
the United States would execute the larger projects, for no
private enterprise could divert such rivers as the Missouri, the
Colorado, or the Platte. And Senator Teller of Colorado

9 *Ibid.*, May 12, 1888, p. 4078; May 14, 1888, p. 4087.
10 U. S., Senate Report No. 1814, 50th Cong., 1st Sess., 114, 128. "Do you
mean to withhold the information for fear that the Government will be
led into something that ought not to be done?" Teller asked. "That is
certainly one reason that would control me," Hale replied. *Ibid.*

gradually betrayed Stewart. First, Teller insisted on the strictly scientific objectives of an irrigation survey. Next, he admitted that some general system of legislation was inevitable. But he barred the government from building the reservoirs. "The people of the States, the States themselves," or capitalists would do the job. Then he lost all caution and blurted out that "the time will come when the government of the United States will have to do what every government in the whole world has done in arid regions—put out its money to build reservoirs."[11]

The lack of provision against speculation seemed another weakness. As Allison explained, his committee was willing to prepare for any eventuality by enlarging the appropriation for mapmaking and by examining methods and cost in the building of irrigation works. What he and his colleagues questioned was the wisdom of spending money for the discovery of reservoir sites or canal lines if an enterprising citizen could locate himself on these sites or lines (which he was entitled to do under the laws of the United States), later forcing the government to pay a large sum for his property.[12] Another possibility was that the irrigable lands discovered by scientists of the Survey would also bring the speculators swarming.

The managers of the bill appealed the decision of the committee on appropriations, and this final parliamentary maneuver was successful. On July 30 the Senate approved the irrigation survey as an amendment from the floor by Bowen to the Sundry Civil Appropriation Bill.[13] Later in the summer this bill was returned to the House.

The House was visionary and demonstrative; it wanted to act in the spirit of the homestead legislation. Many members were expecting that an irrigation survey would give the

[11] U. S., *Congressional Record,* 50th Cong., 1st Sess., July 30, 1888, p. 7018.
[12] *Ibid.,* 7016.
[13] *Ibid.,* 7032.

poor man a farm and thus realize the destiny of the republic in the West. Again and again they applauded their best orators on this stirring theme. S. S. Cox of New York described "our progressive people" as "seeking ever the Westward ho! and the Star of Empire."[14] According to J. J. O'Neill of Missouri, the irrigation bill was in the same generous spirit as the legislation to organize the Oklahoma Territory, which labor unions were advocating through petitions bearing thousands of signatures. Both measures meant opportunity for the workingmen in the public domain. Marcus Smith electrified his audience with a plea to "redeem the arid regions," "make homes for your people," and "save your lands from monopoly."[15]

Intending to fight speculation, the House planned an exciting and controversial revision. G. G. Symes of Colorado and W. C. P. Breckinridge of Kentucky attached an amendment to the Powell bill, withdrawing from sale or entry all the valuable lands of the public domain discovered by scientific research. The Breckinridge amendment, as it was called, read as follows: "And all the lands which may hereafter be designated or selected by such United States surveys for sites for reservoirs, ditches, or canals for irrigation purposes and all the lands made susceptible of irrigation by such reservoirs, ditches, or canals, are from this time henceforth hereby reserved from sale as the property of the United States, and shall not be subject after the passage of this act to entry, settlement, or occupation until further provided by law."[16]

W. S. Holman, chairman of the committee on the public lands, reminded everyone how radical this reservation clause was. It suspended the operation of the major land laws in the western states and territories, for until the Geological Survey classified the land, no one could be sure that any particular parcel did or did not come within the terms of the irrigation

14 *Ibid.*, September 1, 1888, p. 8202.
15 *Ibid.*, September 10, 1888, pp. 8475, 8478.
16 *Ibid.*, September 1, 1888, p. 8200. Another section of the amend-

law. Holman worried about the effect on the Desert Land Act, which was then the most popular vehicle for transferring public land to private ownership. "Are you prepared," he asked the House, "on such slight investigations as we have had, such hasty inquiry and such partial knowledge of the facts," to stop the activity "which in a comparatively short period of time has . . . entered over 5,000,000 acres of this so-called 'desert land'?" Symes, one of the framers of the amendment, promptly backed down. The entire arid region embracing one-third of the national area could not be reserved, he said. It was enough to tell the homesteader that he might have to permit a ditch through his farm or lose part of it to a reservoir. A bill to withdraw irrigable lands would "stop the emigration to the West . . . stop progress, stop the settling up of the country, and you can not do that."[17] The eloquence of Marcus Smith ebbed away into timidity. Now he saw "an embargo on the prosperity of my constituents." If Arizona was ever to be reclaimed, it must happen under a reasonable desert land law, "such as we now have."[18]

The House majority stood firm. It insisted on the Powell-Breckinridge bill, though it conceded to Herbert and other economy-minded Democrats a reduction of the appropriation to $100,000. It ignored Teller's complaint that "we should be worse off than if we had nothing at all."[19] And in committee its representatives forced the senatorial conferees to yield, despite confident predictions to the contrary. The best that Senator Allison could do was to insert a final stipulation that the

ment required that "the Director of the Geological Survey . . . shall make a report to Congress . . . showing in detail how the said money has been expended, the amount used for actual survey and engineer work in the field in locating sites for reservoirs, and an itemized account of the expenditure under this appropriation . . ."

[17] *Ibid.*, September 11, 1888, pp. 8507, 8510. Holman also wanted to know how the measure affected the land grants to the continental railroads.

[18] *Ibid.*, September 19, 1888, Appendix, 579.

[19] *Ibid.*, September 12, 1888, p. 8543.

THE ARID REGION

President could open the reserved lands to homestead settlement. On October 2, 1888, the irrigation survey became the
law of the land.[20]

Powell planned to do the topographical mapping in units
called catchment areas or hydrographic basins. He identified
these units provisionally by their location on a typical drainage system, occupying a portion of the main stem, a tributary,
or an upper branch. The interest of Teller and Stewart influenced greatly the selection of specific districts for topographic
development. Half of the mapping was done in Colorado, and
a substantial force of topographers also worked in Nevada.
Anton Karl immediately began work in the foothills around
Denver, which Teller knew from his hunting days. After two
months there Karl joined other mapmakers in the valley of
the Arkansas River, who were moving south and east from
the vicinity of Leadville to the Kansas line. W. D. Johnson
directed this operation, which covered 20,000 square miles in
one sustained drive ending in November 1889. H. M. Wilson
was sent to map along the upper parts of the Truckee, Carson,
and Walker Rivers in Nevada. The second year he was assisted
by other topographers who started in California and passed
the crest of the Sierra Nevada to enter the basin of Lake
Tahoe and Carson Valley. Along the Rio Grande, where
Powell went because irrigation was already established, most
of the workers began near Albuquerque and Santa Fé. They
mapped a block of territory embracing on the west the Jemez
and Chama Rivers, tributaries of the Rio Grande, and on the
east the headwaters of the Pecos and Canadian Rivers.

Mapping led quickly to one of the primary objectives.
Powell believed that his topographers, given their knowledge
of distances, altitudes, and slopes, would be able to find and

[20] U. S., *Statutes at Large,* XXV (1887-1889), 527.

record reservoir sites, which might be located almost anywhere in a catchment area—on the plains, in the foothills, or in the mountains. He made the first selections himself by going to the valley of the Rio Grande and picking out six places for reservoirs along the Jemez River. When he appeared before the Senate committee on appropriations in February 1889 he brought along a topographical map with the six locations marked in blue; "I did it in a hurry," he explained to the committee, "so as to have something to show," so that "you may know what the survey is to be."[21] The mapmakers reported more than 150 reservoir sites, along with estimates on heights, capacities, and even materials. This requirement that the topographers also be construction engineers, and Powell's insistence that the topographical maps saved substantial labor in the location of canal lines, led later to open conflict with the engineering division.

The hydrographic division to measure flow of streams began as a school and a workshop. Powell could not hire any of the two dozen persons in the United States who knew anything about measuring streams, nor did he have the use of standardized instruments or advanced methods. Powell's staff spent the preparatory stage at Embudo, New Mexico, on the Rio Grande north of Santa Fé, and just before Christmas 1888 Dutton, who was divisional chief, reported that his 14 "young men" had made a rope ferry on a raft and were gauging the Rio Grande.[22] They practiced on several kinds of water meters, tested evaporating vessels, and studied ways of measuring sediment. A visiting professor lectured on climatology. In the spring of 1889, 12 graduates scattered over the arid region, following the topographers through the valley of the Rio Grande, where six gauging stations were located, to the Arkansas River in Colorado, to the Carson and Truckee Rivers

21 U. S., Senate Report No. 2613, 50th Cong., 2nd Sess., 113, 106.
22 C. E. Dutton to J. W. Powell, December 21, 1888, U. S. Geological Survey, Letters Received, 1888.

in Nevada, and to the Sun and Yellowstone Rivers in Montana. At several places the hydrographers arrived first—in the basin of the Snake River, along the Gila and Salt Rivers in Arizona, and in Utah—where 14 gauging stations were established.

The engineering division was Congress' idea. During the prelegislative discussion, Powell admitted that he had never figured the cost of reservoirs as he felt that subject lay outside the scope of his work. But when the House in its farflung amendment stipulated a report on the money "used for actual survey and engineer work in the field in locating sites for reservoirs," he had no choice.[23] After the arrangements had been made for mapmaking and water-gauging the first year, there was $7,000 left, which was enough to prepare engineering parties for the field in 1889. The second year a larger share ($60,000 out of $250,000) went to this division. The scientific results by the spring of 1890 were 35 reservoir sites fully surveyed and 400 lines of canal surveyed. According to Dutton, who again was in charge, the ideal locations were in Montana near the three forks of the Missouri River and in the valleys of the Sun and Yellowstone Rivers. There during the spring of 1889 H. M. Wilson, promoted from the topographic division, traveled 2,000 miles on horseback and 1,600 by rail with only a hand level in his pocket looking for reservoir sites. Wilson wanted places for safe and inexpensive dams, where water supply and arable land were in close proximity.[24] Along the Sun River, which joins the Missouri from the west at Great Falls, Montana, Wilson planned a network of nine reservoirs, which he tied into three diversion canals, one 40 miles long. He gave details on the location of dams, their size and height, waste weirs, materials of construction (loose rock, ma-

---

[23] See above, fn. 16.

[24] C. E. Dutton to W. M. Stewart, March 31, 1890, U.S., Senate Report No. 928, 51st Cong., 1st Sess., Part 5, p. 148. See also, "Engineering — Montana Division," U.S.G.S. *Eleventh Annual Report*, Part II, *Irrigation*, 113-33. Wilson estimated costs at $10,000 to $40,000 per reservoir.

sonry, or clay earth), grade of canal lines, and costs. Dutton also respected the work of the Snake River division under A. D. Foote, who once had mapped for Emmons at Leadville. Foote recommended Jackson Lake, Wyoming, and a site at Swan Valley, across the Wyoming border into Idaho. At Eagle Rock (Idaho Falls) below the junction of the two forks of the Snake, he planned two grand canals—the one on the north side to extend 200 miles and serve a million acres; the other on the south to be 70 miles long and reach 200,000 acres. American Falls, farther west on the Snake River, seemed made by nature for a reservoir. After running two canal lines, Foote reluctantly concluded that cost made the site impractical.[25] He found Minidoka Ferry satisfactory, and today this site has a government reservoir on it. There is one also at American Falls, but not at Eagle Rock.

The irrigation survey always meant more to Powell than the assembling of scientific or engineering facts. He hoped that it would promote establishment of a new government unit, which he had first proposed in his *Lands of the Arid Region*. He intended to publicize his opinion that the arid region divided naturally into catchment areas and that these catchment areas, or irrigation districts, were the foundation of all important economic and political activity. Every district, he said, was "a body of interdependent and unified interests and values, all collected in one hydrographic basin, and all segregated by well-defined boundary lines from the rest of the world."[26] Topographic mapping discovered the area of these geographic units and defined their boundaries. The hydrographic divi-

25 "I have concluded to set a limit for the guidance of the men at work in the field," Powell said to the committee on appropriations of the Senate in 1889; "they must not select a reservoir site and set it apart if it will not store water at a cost of $25 per acre." U. S., Senate Report No. 2613, 50th Cong., 2nd Sess., 114. Powell explained the figure of $25 thus: "it must be understood that an acre of land irrigated is at once worth from $30 to $200 an acre." *Ibid.*

26 "Institutions for the Arid Lands," *Century Illustrated Monthly Magazine*, XL (1890), 114.

sion evaluated the water resources of each district. To avoid controversy these resources must originate and be used within the district; there could be no reliance on other districts or responsibility to them. The engineering information led to the reservoir sites of the district, and to the canal lines, which must be projected entirely within the natural boundaries. Future surveys to pinpoint the tracts of irrigable land were planned. The knowledge discovered by the irrigation survey assured the success of government and society in the arid region. The farming people of each district could organize and manage their own community's natural resources, drafting rules for protection and use of these resources. If they wanted to control the water by themselves, they knew how "in a thoroughly economic manner." If they engaged corporations to do the work for them, they could "make the contracts with intelligence."[27] They lived in communities scattered up and down a river valley, practicing irrigation on small farms of 40 to 80 acres, which were adjacent to unoccupied areas of grass, timber, or water.

No experiment was ever permitted to test this ideal society or the integrity of the scientific knowledge intended to shape it. There are some indications, however, that the geographical facts were not as compelling as Powell would have liked them to be. The physical framework, upon which so much depended, was incomplete. The director outlined 100 of the catchment areas on a large, brilliantly colored map,[28] but he passed over many areas for lack of definitive boundaries. The valleys of the Colorado River and Rio Grande seemed impossible to partition. His famous statement that physical conditions "inexorably control" human operations suggests that he was expecting geography to guide and sanction all economic and

27 U. S., Senate Report No. 928, 51st Cong., 1st Sess., Part 5, p. 200.
28 This irrigation district map is reproduced in all its colors, but on a much smaller scale in U.S.G.S. *Eleventh Annual Report,* Part II, *Irrigation,* Plate LXIX.

political conduct in the arid region.[29] Apparently he did not
mean that man was bound to the physiographical pattern, for
he admitted that settlers could disrupt the economy of a catchment area, and he specifically warned against cutting timber
near a reservoir or pirating water before it reached the land
designated as irrigable. Adaptation to the arid region was not
predetermined by geographical circumstances; it came through
human organization and effort. Because some pioneers would
not respect the natural equilibrium within an irrigation district, the others must exercise collective power to restrain
them. Powell also gave arguments for his form of collectivism,
which had nothing to do with geographical knowledge or influence. The federal government should not construct the irrigation works, for this would mean "nationalizing the agricultural institutions of the arid country."[30] A bureau of forestry to
guard the drainage area would turn into "an army of aliens"
and a "hotbed of corruption." Let the people of the irrigation
district do the work themselves, because every one of them was
"a freeman king with power to rule himself, and they may be
trusted with their own interests."[31] Furthermore, the local way
was more "in harmony with the institutions of this country."[32]
One of the most ambitious attempts ever made to legislate on
the basis of geographical determinism ended with an appeal
to historical tradition.

In 1890 Congress repudiated Powell's leadership in irrigation affairs and abolished his survey. The new departure began
within a select committee of senators, who were charged with
discovering the best mode of reclaiming the arid lands. Actu-

29 "The Non-Irrigable Lands of the Arid Region," *Century Illustrated
Monthly Magazine,* XXXIX (1890), 922.

30 "The Arid Lands," U.S.G.S. *Eleventh Annual Report,* Part II, *Irrigation,* 255.

31 "Institutions for the Arid Lands," *Century Illustrated Monthly Magazine,* XL (1890), 114, 115.

32 J. W. Powell, "The Arid Lands," 255.

ally, the committee's work was aimed at discrediting Powell, which it undertook to do during 10 sessions in January and March. First, two members of the committee, L. R. Casey of North Dakota and G. C. Moody of South Dakota, complained bitterly because a government survey of water supply in the arid region had not included artesian resources of their states. These resources were so extensive, they said, that well-digging in the valleys of the James and Missouri Rivers would reveal underground reservoirs. Senator Moody wondered why the director wandered off into uninhabited regions. The average citizen knew and cared nothing about a topographical survey. A formidable convert was Senator Stewart, chairman of the committee, who said the irrigation survey would be a long time in preparation, and the people wanted immediate knowledge or relief.

In his replies Powell stressed the weakness of popular enthusiasm and the general limitations of artesian water resources. He said the people saw streams of water bursting out of the ground and shooting high into the air, and "in times of drought these are wonderful scenes." Hopefully, they took this as evidence of an underground river or lake, when only modest amounts of water were percolating through sedimentary rock. Scientists knew that Dakota sandstone stored most of the artesian water in the Great Plains, but they had yet to circumscribe the boundaries of this sandstone or determine its capacity. Let the productive strata be mapped and selective well-digging undertaken. Then the government could say with authority: "bore here and you will get water . . . do not bore there because you can not get water."[33] He predicted rapid exhaustion if indiscriminate digging were encouraged; worldwide experience showed that if too many wells were sunk in any basin, all were thereby destroyed.

Any advantage which these sound remarks gave him Powell

33 U. S., Senate Report No. 928, 51st Cong., 1st Sess., Part 5, pp. 87, 89, 94.

lost by disparagement of artesian water resources in general. The water from porous rock would never be enough to irrigate any large tracts of land. If all the wells on every continent were assembled in the Dakotas, "they would not irrigate a county of land," he said.[34] As a source of water supply, artesian fountains could not compare with storm waters or even with sand reservoirs dug in the channels of lost rivers. Later that year Moody with some justification accused Powell of giving "our scheme a black eye at the outset" by declaring that artesian basins "would not amount to anything."[35]

This exchange exposed a geographical anomaly and political weakness of the irrigation survey. Conceptually, Powell had considered the arid region to be the area in western United States where the annual rainfall was less than 20 inches. But his Survey operated only in the eight states and territories which were the heartland of the region, bypassing the outlying states on the Pacific coast, and, even more important, an eastern group (Kansas, Nebraska, and the two Dakotas), through which he had drawn the 20-inch line of rainfall, near the one hundredth meridian. Water supply in these four states was not studied, although they were growing more rapidly than many places to the west and suffered more from drought. Powell frequently advised people of this marginal area, but he had no program for them.[36]

Continuing their challenge of Powell's work, Stewart, Moody, and Casey invited testimony from those in the engineering division, who hated an irrigation survey devoted primarily to topographical mapping. This invitation broke one of the standing relationships between the Geological Survey and Congress, whereby public and formal negotiations

34 *Ibid.*, 46.
35 U.S., House Report No. 2407, 51st Cong., 1st Sess., 74.
36 *Official Report of the Proceedings and Debates of the First Constitutional Convention of North Dakota* (1889), 410-11.

from the side of the executive remained in the hands of the director. Once Representative Herbert had called this custom tyrannical and dictatorial. On the defensive Powell asked that other persons in the irrigation survey, who favored his management, be heard. Stewart suggested submission in writing of the opinions favorable to Powell, but Senator J. K. Jones of the Democratic minority objected to "one-sided testimony."[37] The result was a convergence upon the committee on irrigation of two opposing groups of scientists, which raised the level of congressional discussion about Survey science to its highest peak.

The most persistent disagreement was the utility of the topographical maps. Powell, Gilbert, and W. D. Johnson argued that these maps saved labor and expense in the location of the lines of canals. Ordinarily, engineers selected promising places by simple observation. Then they tested their selections by running trial lines, which meant mapping narrow corridors as alternative locations for the canals. This trial line method was expensive, requiring parties of transitmen and levelers. "It costs on an average $25 per mile to run a trial line on the ground," Powell said; "altogether hundreds of thousands, perhaps more than a million miles of trial lines would have to be run if this method were to be adopted." Powell favored letting the trial-line maps be replaced by the topographical maps of the irrigation survey, which were constructed at a saving of 50 percent or more. Using them, the field engineers could plan or project the lines of canals with "as fair a degree of accuracy and certainty as if they were actually run by transit and level." Gilbert said that railroad building was done in the Appalachian region without trial lines; engineers did not

[37] The quotations from the committee discussion about the topographical mapping of the irrigation survey are to be found in U. S., Senate Report No. 928, 51st Cong., 1st Sess., Part 5, pp. 135, 142, 146, 154, 167, 170, 183, 184, 193, 195, 202, 210, 212.

survey or map all possible routes in determining the best. They compared routes through the Survey maps and moved immediately into the construction stage.

Dutton, who directed the division of engineering, which was supposed to value and use the topographical maps, was an old friend and colleague of Powell's. However, he testified that maps which suited the engineers were not attainable through the methods used by the topographic division. The topographers were making a general map, while the engineers needed detail. A survey to establish the line of a canal must plan for a horizontal scale of "never less" than 1,000 feet to the inch, and "more frequently" of 100 or 200 feet to the inch, whereas a general topographic map meant a survey upon a scale of 10,000 feet to the inch. According to Reagan of Texas, now a senator and a member of the committee, the vertical element in the topographical mapping of the Survey was expressed through contour intervals of 4 feet. Dutton corrected him. As far as he knew, the plan was for 20-foot contours in the valleys, 50-foot in the hills, and 100-foot in the mountains. These scales could not possibly serve the engineers, who, as it turned out, made their own reports with contour intervals from 2 to 10 feet.

When Powell was cross with Dutton who, he said, "never made a topographic map," the select committee called S. H. Bodfish of the engineering division, who had been constructing maps for the Survey since its beginning in 1879. Bodfish judged his topographical work in Massachusetts as useless for developing the line of a canal. He scoffed at the idea that engineers ran innumerable, expensive trial lines. Rather they examined the country by eye, selected the promising sites for canals, and surveyed those sites alone. His picture of their field work resembled closely the actual operations of H. M. Wilson in Montana during the summer of 1889 which Dutton had praised so highly. Bodfish rejected any analogy with railroad building. There was a great difference between a ditch line and a railroad line. A ditch line was "a rigid line" and could not be "determined by anything but the lightest grades," he explained. A railroad line was not rigid; "it is covered by a variety of grades, steep and light." This flexibility of grade made possible its location by a general map, whereas the grade of a canal to transport water was slight and inflexible. An engineer needed more detail, which he secured by running a trial line.

Having learned from the engineers that an irrigation survey without topographical mapping was possible, the senators attacked Powell on new ground. The director was authorized under the irrigation act of 1888 "to make the necessary maps." If his topographical maps were unnecessary, then they represented an illegal expenditure of public monies, and Powell was a lawbreaker. The committee never succeeded, however, in establishing a scientific meaning for the words "necessary maps," which clearly excluding the topographical maps made them illegal. Chairman Stewart first proposed that these maps were useless, but an eloquent reply by Powell impressed him, and the answers of the engineers made his position untenable. The director eulogized the topographic division: "I have employed a corps of men of ability and genius," he boasted. They used their technical genius to make the necessary geographical observations within a drainage or irrigation district. Somebody must "see all of that ground," before the plan was made for storing and carrying water, either the engineer or the topographer for him. By "seeing the ground" Powell said that he meant more than visual observation; the job must be done instrumentally. "No man," he asserted, "can properly estimate distances, altitudes, and slopes without instrumentation." The conscientious observer, if an engineer, recorded his scientific findings in a notebook, the topographer on a map. To put the findings in a notebook took as long as to map them; why not, then, omit the engineer at this stage? "The map is a notebook," he concluded, "the simplest and cheapest method of keeping the records. There it assembles the facts so that they can be seen as a conspectus and their relations known." Dutton admitted that a general map helped an engineer in the selection of reservoir sites; he was led more quickly to the area of a watershed and the crucial knowledge of water flow during floods. Otherwise, he must labor a week or two surveying the drainage basin. Bodfish said that he would study a general map before going into the field; there was much to be learned from it about altitudes, ground slope, and impossible reservoir sites. Topographer Johnson testified that when Bodfish began working in Colorado his request for maps or map data of any kind were "continuous, urgent, and annoyingly persistent." Johnson accommodated Bodfish as best he could, and the division of engineering acknowledged the usefulness of the unfinished material, but as Dutton said in June 1889 "ultimately . . . we must have the thoroughly completed map."

Stewart was no more successful with the argument that, whatever the convenience of topographic maps for an irrigation survey, the word "necessary" in the law had the connotation of "indispensable." Dutton, when asked whether the maps were necessary to the purposes of the irrigation law, replied that they were not; an engineering and hydrographic survey, meeting the requirements of the law, could be conducted without a topographic survey. His men, for example, went into the field without waiting for the topographic division's maps. But he also said that he thought there was no single, authoritative definition of the disputed adjective. Actual usage subtracted substantially from its apparent rigor: "We are every day certifying that certain things are necessary on our bills and on our vouchers. While in a certain sense and in the ordinary acceptation of the term they are necessary, in an absolute sense they are not." And Dutton was a firm believer in the national mapping program of the Survey. "I think no money has been better spent," he said as he left the hearings.

In this technical discussion, which reached a sustained climax during six meetings in March, the view of the engineers prevailed. Dutton and his colleagues rejected the legalistic attitude which the select committee advocated. Approval or disapproval of the irrigation survey did not depend upon subtle interpretations of a common word. The law had not been violated. They were also correct in disputing the claims of Powell for the instrumental precision of his topographic maps. The engineers knew, for example, that in drawing contour lines the Survey topographers depended primarily upon estimates by eye.

The engineers' idea of an irrigation survey was a union of water study and engineering. Sites for water storage were easy to find, but an engineer could not begin work on them until he knew the water supply, lest he construct too many reservoirs. Population trends dictated the choice of the irrigable lands, and water should be carried where people were. Mindful of these modest and immediate objectives, the engineers had little or no sympathy for Powell's comprehensive, regional approach or his desire for systematic study of land, water, and forest reserves, or his enthusiasm for economic planning and collective democracy. An irrigation survey should not map pasture land, said E. S. Nettleton, second in command after Dutton; or outlying regions, Bodfish added. "It does not need to be done in a day," remarked Stewart, "because the land can not all be occupied in a day."

Despite their preference in committee for an engineering survey, Senators Stewart, Moody, Casey, and Plumb were completely negative in the majority report published early in May. The four senators devoted many pages to the condemnation of Powell and the Survey's connection with irrigation. They accused him of misapplying public funds, saying when he spent irrigation survey money on topography, he was adding illegally to the annual appropriation of the Geological Survey. Two laws were cited, the Sundry Civil Appropriation Acts of

October 2, 1888, and March 2, 1889. By the Act of October 2, 1888, $199,000 was appropriated for topographical surveys (part of the annual budget for the Geological Survey, although the senators did not say so) and $100,000 for irrigation surveys. Powell "diverted" $60,000 of the irrigation survey money and added it to the appropriation for topographic surveys, making $259,000 for topography and leaving only $40,000 for irrigation. Similarly, by the Act of March 2, 1889, $200,000 was appropriated for topographic surveys (the budget of the Survey) and $250,000 for irrigation surveys; here Powell "diverted" $120,000 of the irrigation money and added it to the amount for topographic surveys, making $320,000 for topography and leaving only $130,000 for irrigation. This transfer of public money was indefensible, for it was a well-known principle of federal law, expressed in countless opinions of attorney-generals and comptrollers, that whenever Congress appropriated money for a particular purpose, no more could be spent for that purpose unless authorized by the legislative branch. The words "necessary maps" in appropriation acts of 1888 and 1889 were not enough textual support for the authority which Powell had exercised; it was "a most unjustifiable straining of interpretation to conclude that such vague and indefinite words . . . meant so vast and costly an undertaking as a topographic map of the whole arid region."[38] By relying on dubious phraseology Powell had denied to the arid West two-thirds of the benefit of a proper irrigation survey. The committee only pretended about the future, putting the division of engineering in the Department of Agriculture and calling upon the U. S. Army Weather Bureau to gauge streams. This showed no serious, constructive planning for an irrigation survey, simply the determination to get rid of Powell's.

In the final months of the irrigation survey, scientific or technological questions were lost in a storm of senatorial com-

38 *Ibid.*, Part 1, p. 9.

plaint and abuse, which arose because of the House clause in
the law of 1888, reserving from entry, settlement, occupation,
or sale all lands designated by the Geological Survey as valuable for irrigation. This controversial section generally was
withheld until the late spring of 1890, and then its release
threatened the whole public land system.

Officials in the executive branch of government had committed themselves verbally to enforcing the reservation clause
during the summer of 1889, after an angry telegram to the Secretary of the Interior from a constitutional convention meeting
in Idaho.[39] This telegram was about Bear Lake, which lay north
and south across the Idaho-Utah border near Wyoming, and
Bear River, which flowed from the vicinity of the lake in a
northwesterly direction into Idaho and then, turning southward, emptied into the Great Salt Lake. The convention complained that a corporate attempt was afoot to seize Bear Lake
and to control the river for 150 miles in Idaho, monopolizing
water for use in Utah. A startled Secretary of the Interior
directed Powell to survey "with the utmost expedition"[40] all
irrigable lands in the valley of Bear River. Also, Commissioner
W. M. Stone of the General Land Office dispatched a circular
to his registers and receivers, telling them to cancel all entries
or filings made since October 2, 1888, on sites for reservoirs
and canals or on lands which could be irrigated. When the
registers and receivers asked Stone what specific lands were
meant, he answered evasively, so local officials went on taking
the money of applicants or entrymen.[41]

When in the following spring (1890) many of the entries

[39] Memorial of the Idaho Constitutional Convention to the Secretary of
the Interior, August 2, 1889, *Annual Report of the Commissioner of the
General Land Office for the Fiscal Year Ended June 30, 1890* (Washington,
1890), 72-73.

[40] J. W. Powell to the Secretary of the Interior, December 19, 1889,
U. S. Geological Survey, Letters Sent, 1889.

[41] W. M. Stone to Registers and Receivers, United States Land Offices,
August 5, 1889, *Annual Report of the Commissioner of the General Land
Office for the Fiscal Year Ended June 30, 1890*, pp. 71-72. See J. W. Noble
to G. L. Shoup, August 3, 1889, *ibid.*, 70-71.

which Stone's circular theoretically had cancelled were being
sent to Washington for final confirmation of title, the new
commissioner, L. A. Groff, acted to protect his bureau from
any political or legal embarrassment. He did not communicate, as Stone had, with the receivers and registers, who during
June and July continued to accept the money of entrymen
and issue receipts. Instead he circulated a memorandum in
his Washington office, to the effect that no entry or filing upon
lands in the arid region would be approved for patenting until
further notice. Within 24 hours this memorandum "brought
forth an expression" from western senators and representatives.[42] Groff through channels passed the problem on to William Howard Taft, Solicitor General and Acting Attorney
General, who announced his ruling on May 24, 1890. It was
the purpose of Congress, he wrote, to suspend all rights of
entry upon any lands which might possibly come within the
scope of the law of 1888; "language could hardly be stronger
than are the words of the act in expressing this intention."
Taft warned against interpreting a law in the light of its consequences. However far-reaching these consequences were, they
could not deprive words "of their ordinary and necessary
meaning."[43] The executive department should not shirk its
duty, even though it meant closing every land office in the
country.

Taft's ruling turned most of the Senate against the irrigation law and drove a score of the western members into fa-
natical opposition. A. S. Paddock of Nebraska saw "one of the
wickedest pieces of legislation that has ever been enacted by
Congress,"[44] J. N. Dolph of Oregon called the reservation
clause a national "curse,"[45] and Stewart, who blamed himself

42 U. S., Senate Report No. 1466, 51st Cong., 1st Sess., 33.

43 W. H. Taft to the Secretary of the Interior, May 24, 1890, *Annual
Report of the Commissioner of the General Land Office for the Fiscal
Year Ended June 30, 1890*, p. 63.

44 U. S., *Congressional Record*, 51st Cong., 1st Sess., August 8, 1890, p.
8324.

45 *Ibid.*, August 26, 1890, p. 9155.

for the "calamity," promised to "liberate" the western country.[46] W. F. Sanders of Montana boasted that he could "go
to-morrow to the State of Montana and march one-half of her
citizens on foot . . . to the City of Washington to petition
for the repeal of the [irrigation] law." And these petitioners
would be, first, the men without homes "who want them," and
second, "the men who have homes and want neighbors, and
know they have the land for them."[47] T. C. Power, Sanders'
colleague from Montana, said that the people of the state
much preferred public land surveys to irrigation surveys. Action to suspend the traditional surveys astonished the senator,
in the face of his constant "begging and asking" for their
expansion.[48]

The senators soon learned that they would have to fight for
repeal. Several of them asked President Benjamin Harrison to
exercise his option under the law of 1888 and declare all reserved lands open to homestead settlement, but the chief executive would not act. How could he accommodate them, he
asked, and still reserve the irrigable lands and reservoir sites,
when he had yet to learn the location of either? Moreover,
when the lands and sites were discovered, they must be segregated until the rights of the public in them had been determined.[49] A visit by Stewart and Moody to the House
committee on appropriations also failed, for after listening to
the two senators the committee voted the irrigation survey an
increase of half a million dollars for the next fiscal year. And
on June 13 a motion from the floor of the House to eliminate
the appropriation was defeated, 67 to 45.[50] The representatives still wanted the small proprietor to be the beneficiary of
land distribution in the arid region. The real issue between

[46] *Ibid.,* July 16, 1890, p. 7321; U. S., House Report No. 2407, 51st Cong.,
1st Sess., 63.
[47] U. S., Senate Report No. 1466, 51st Cong., 1st Sess., 122-23.
[48] *Ibid.,* 85.
[49] *Ibid.,* 112.
[50] U. S., *Congressional Record,* 51st Cong., 1st Sess., June 15, 1890, p. 6059.

the Senate and the House, Breckinridge of Kentucky said during the summer, was "whether that territory so large, so capable of culture, so full of promise, so magnificent in hope,
shall belong to the speculators who desire to own it, or to the
common people."[51] Representative Holman, who had defended
the Desert Land Act in 1888, now characterized it as a "wild
riot of fraud, monopoly, and speculation"; only the grants to
railroad corporations had been worse. Holman predicted "imperial estates" in the West, if the law was allowed to continue.[52] And he told his colleagues that the Senate had made
only one concession of recent years toward proper legislation
on the public domain—the irrigation law of 1888.

The third force in the way of the Senate was Director
Powell, who, in the worst mistake of his public career, declared for the Taft ruling. He had always been willing to say
that rich men and stock companies were appropriating the
streams of the arid region; now in the spring of 1890 he amplified and reiterated this accusation. "All the lands and all
the waters are coming under the control of companies at a
rapid rate, at the rate of millions of dollars annually," he told
the committee on irrigation of the House.[53] He assured the
committee on appropriations of the same branch that in five
states or territories large blocs of land were held by persons
and corporations, and that in these same five places big water
companies controlled irrigation.[54] He revealed that persons
and corporations were urging their plans for water development upon him. His answer to these private plans was that
they negated the comprehensive, scientific treatment of hydrographic basins and allowed capitalistic promoters to reap the
rewards. Also, the law of 1888 forbade him to endorse or
advertise irrigation schemes, however deserving, which con-

51 *Ibid.,* July 25, 1890, p. 7724.
52 *Ibid.,* July 26, 1890, pp. 7766-68.
53 J. W. Powell, "The Arid Lands," 237.
54 U. S., House Report No. 2407, 51st Cong., 1st Sess., 66. The five states
or territories were Colorado, Nevada, New Mexico, Arizona, and California.

centrated land and water in the hands of a few persons or corporations. The Taft ruling, Powell said, would allow the irrigable lands to be located, and then the President could open them to settlement under the homestead law, the land act most favorable to the common man.[55]

By declaring in favor of reservation Powell exposed himself to massive attack from the Senate. This began early in July at the hearings of the committee on appropriations, attended by eight senators who were not members. Moody wanted to know who had made the reservation, Powell or the General Land Office. Powell answered that the law reserved the lands. The Gallatin Valley of Montana was good land, Power said, talking about his home state, and "your taking that out or reserving it for reservoir purposes is a great hardship to the people." Moody wondered why Powell excluded settlers from the Black Hills of South Dakota, which were as well watered, he lied, as any part of New York or New England. Eastern Washington was productive wheat country, J. B. Allen said, and should not have been withdrawn. J. N. Dolph called the Grande Ronde in northeastern Oregon the finest valley on earth; yet it had been reserved. "Why draw an arbitrary line [the one hundredth meridian]," and tie up "nearly one-half of the state of Nebraska?" A. S. Paddock asked.[56]

The hostile senators tried to trap Powell through his most recent map of the arid region, which in bright colors outlined the drainage or irrigation districts so far identifiable. Since Powell had done all his coloring west of the one hundred and first or the one hundred and second meridian, he, in effect, deserted the original eastern boundary along the isohyetal line of 20 inches of precipitation, at the one hundredth meridian. Commissioner Groff, who needed to know the locus of the irrigable lands and had been following Powell's earlier and broader definition of the arid region, asked for a copy of the

[55] J. W. Powell, "The Arid Lands," 286.
[56] This exchange between Powell and the senators is to be found in U. S., Senate Report No. 1466, 51st Cong., 1st Sess., 61, 84, 94, 95, 103, 108.

new map, saying he would be guided by it. The senators accused the director of using his "beautiful" map to reserve the
entire West, but Powell successfully contradicted this charge.
He had constructed the map for the use of the Congress (it
later hung in the Senate chamber). When asked, he had made
a copy for Commissioner Groff, but he did not know whether
or not this copy was actually being used in the business of the
General Land Office, as he had not been consulted. The map
represented his personal idea of the arid region, not a legal
interpretation of it.

Mystified, Chairman Allison asked Powell, "now where,
when, and how do we know that certain lands are included
in the act of October 2, 1888; and certain lands are not?"

"There has been no decision rendered on that subject by
anybody that I know of—the Secretary [of the Interior] or
anybody else," Powell replied.

"How then does it come that any portion of these lands are
withdrawn?" Allison asked. "Somebody must know where these
lands are located," he exclaimed. "I want to know who is it
that fixes the arid regions."

Senator Hale thought that the Department of the Interior
located them, using the findings of the irrigation survey and
"the theories and opinions" of Director Powell. However,
Powell, leader of the irrigation survey, had just disclaimed
authoritative knowledge of the disputed lands.

There never was any doubt that Allison's committee would
strike out the appropriation by the House for the irrigation
survey, and later in July the Senate as a whole spent four days
explaining why this was done. So overwhelming was the sentiment against Powell that his friends on the minority side of
the committee saw no point in moving a favorable amendment
from the floor. The members of the engineering division had
the last word in their disagreement with Powell. Their method
was a long, anonymous letter, "from one of the ablest engineers of the United States Army." This letter, read by Senator
Moody, showed a deep dislike among Powell's engineers of a

feature of the irrigation survey which had not been considered explicitly during the select committee hearings, that is, the requirement that topographers select reservoir sites. The engineers expressed great contempt for these topographers, whom Powell had called "men of genius." The letter described the topographers as "boys, nineteen to twenty-four years of age, fresh from school, who have only to enter the topographical corps of the Geological Survey to become at once endowed with the transcendent quality of mind called genius, able to settle at the rate of a thousand square miles a month the crucial questions of construction, cost, and applicability involved in the determination of a great system of irrigating works." Powell seemed to think that "these boys" could solve all the complex problems of an irrigation survey and that skilled engineers should accept the findings of these young "men of genius" and work out the details. The unknown army engineer faltered only once, when he accused Powell of misusing public funds to realize his personal ambition of constructing a national map, which "will bear his name and be his monument."[57] The accusation of ambition was true, but Powell had done nothing illegal. The Senate dismissed the select committee's conclusion that money had been "squarely misappropriated" and "in direct violation of law."[58] Stewart had won approval in May for a resolution of inquiry to the Secretary of the Interior concerning this diversion of funds, and now in the debates of July he was at it again. J. C. Spooner of Wisconsin, although fearing the competition from reclaimed lands, denied that Powell had violated the law, and G. F. Edmunds of Vermont thought it "a waste of time" even to bring up the subject.[59] The official disposal of the charge did not, however, stop its circulation for many years in Washington and the West.

[57] U. S., *Congressional Record*, 51st Cong., 1st Sess., July 17, 1890, pp. 7345-46.
[58] Senator Stewart's words when the Secretary of the Interior replied to his resolution of inquiry. *Ibid.*, June 4, 1890, p. 5590.
[59] *Ibid.*, July 16, 1890, p. 7328, July 15, 1890, p. 7285.

Senators favored the Desert Land Act to encourage private investment in irrigation, and the reservation clause was a grave threat to the effectiveness of this act. Teller told of the Pecos Irrigation and Investment Company in the New Mexico Territory, which had invested $700,000 in the construction of an irrigation canal and $1 million in roadbuilding as an illustration of what private investors might do. A friend of the senator, J. J. Hagerman, was president of the company. Hagerman knew of the irrigation law, but his lawyers had advised him that it did not apply. The receiver of the land office at Las Cruces went on taking money and issuing receipts for entries, never having been instructed by Washington to do otherwise. Thousands of settlers made their applications for the 640-acre sections, as required by the Desert Land Act, paid the 25 cents an acre enabling them to occupy their holdings, and signed a contract with the company for water delivery. Two hundred thousand acres were thus secured, and in two years the population of Pecos Valley rose from 5,000 to 15,000. Taft's opinion caused alarm, for it pointed to the ruin of both the settlers and the company. If the settlers could not get title to the land, they had no use for the company's water, and then the company could earn no revenue from its ditch.

The Senate was complacent about corruption and monopoly. There was such a thing as being "too nice and too wise," Plumb said. What if the pioneer did ignore the details of land law, exercising "that American directness which always adopts the easiest and cheapest road to the end." What if he did take advantage of the government? "Who is there," who presents a claim before Congress, who expects that claim "to be tried in the same way that it would [be] if it were . . . against an individual?" Plumb asked.[60]

Teller said monopoly existed primarily in ranching; cattle companies seized the land adjacent to a stream and thus con-

60 *Ibid.,* July 16, 1890, Appendix, 720-22.

trolled the country for miles around. Stewart's experience told him that even the land companies with "Mexican grants" must colonize them before they could make any money.[61] At the largest irrigation enterprise in California, Haggin and Carr's on the Kern River, land was being sold with the water right attached.[62] Teller admitted that a company in Colorado had once levied $30 an acre on farmers for tapping its canal and then charged for the water itself. But the legislature eventually prohibited this practice, and thereafter farmers paid for consumption alone.

The senators derided Powell's colony towns or village communities. Plumb called them "newfangled," "medieval," and "un-American"; Allen of Washington, "Utopian" and "experimental"; Morgan of Alabama, "Russian" and "communal." The words "patriarchal" and "paternal" were also hurled. This namecalling was in defense of Plumb's opinion that "every American citizen wants what he owns segregated and separated from the holdings of every other person in the world."[63]

The fervor of the Senate had an effect. When the Sundry Civil Bill was returned to the House at the end of July without the disputed appropriation, the representatives decided against fighting in conference committee to restore the irrigation survey. Their idealism seemed to lack the sustained power that knowledge of geographical or economic realities might have provided; it was too casual or sentimental. The lower legislature had never taken seriously the social ramifications of irrigation. To most representatives Powell's survey meant simply the opportunity to reenact a better and purer homestead law. Once again they glorified the common man of the westward movement, or denounced speculation and monopoly, but no one attempted to explain the importance of proper use of water,

---

[61] U. S., Senate Report No. 1466, 51st Cong., 1st Sess., 119.

[62] J. W. Powell, "The Arid Lands," 237.

[63] For this paragraph see U.S., *Congressional Record*, 51st Cong., 1st Sess., July 17, 18, 1890, pp. 7353, 7406; Appendix, 720-21.

or to outline the institutional changes which geographical conditions made desirable.

The House was also disappointing on the problem of financing irrigation projects. The majority denied that the government should build the works. At the same time this majority was hostile to the Desert Land Act, which had attractive features for private capital. If, for example, 10 men cooperated under this legislation to build a reservoir and canal, their premium or reward was 6,400 acres, which they could then dispose of as reclaimed land. "How," Marcus Smith asked the House, "are you going to settle desert land situated 50 miles from water by any homestead entry?" Smith insisted that the people of the Southwest wanted to be left alone in their struggle with the desert. He noted the proceedings of two "mass meetings" in Pima and Yuma counties in the Arizona Territory where resolutions were adopted calling Taft's opinion "a fatal blow to prosperity" and a barrier to outside investment. People with money would "locate here," read one statement, only if their entries under the Desert Land Act were not disturbed.[64]

The House influenced only such marginal issues as the disposal of the reservoir sites and the maximum size of the land parcels conveyed by the government to its citizens. The settler could live to be as old as Methuselah and never get his vote for more than 160 acres, said Representative J. G. Cannon. Republicans applauded. Representative Cannon was concerned that capitalists should not gain possession of all the water in half of the United States and "levy blackmail . . . through all time upon the men who work on the land irrigated."[65] He disclosed his conversation with another representative, who wanted the reservoir sites returned to the public domain. If the capitalists drew the line too tight, this representative said, the people of the states would pass laws condemning the reservoir sites. Cannon "turned on him" and said

64 *Ibid.,* July 30, 1890, p. 7929; Appendix, 585-86.
65 *Ibid.,* July 30, 1890, p. 7932. See also, July 25, 1892, p. 7726.

this was exactly what should be avoided; let Congress guarantee that the people could utilize the reservoir sites without having to pay for them later through condemnation. In conference committee, where the appropriation for the irrigation survey was eliminated after "eight or ten" sessions, the managers for the House and Senate agreed on setting aside the reservoir sites. Also, no settler could under any one law enter upon more than 320 acres of the public domain.[66]

Ironically, the troublesome clause reserving the arid region became effective less than one month before the law's repeal. The local offices, which Commissioner Groff never had closed, attracted Senator Reagan's attention, and he demanded full enforcement of the law. On August 9, Groff told local receivers and registers they were not to permit entry or filing on any lands lying within the arid region. This order amounted to no more than a gesture, for on September 5 the commissioner rescinded his own circular. In October Arnold Hague informed a colleague that "the Irrigation fellows" had gone; only three persons, he wrote, were "saved from the wreck."[67]

The failure of the irrigation survey was the result of unmanageable political issues, having their origin in scientific research. Repeatedly, the House and Senate clashed over the meaning of this research for the public land system. Powell stirred up more controversy with the emphasis of his inquiry and its revolutionary objectives. He antagonized unnecessarily 20 senators by disparaging the artesian water interest, and he ignored the faith of the Southwest in individual initiative. His statements about the monopolistic tendency of private capital were likely to drive away the investors whom everyone, including Powell, was counting on for building the irrigation works.

If Powell's scientific knowledge and political reform had

66 U.S., *Statutes at Large*, XXVI (1889-1891), 391.
67 Arnold Hague to J. P. Iddings, October 11, 1890, U.S. Geological Survey, Hague Letter Books.

been accepted, would western history have been different? Much depended upon the durability of his sociogeographic communities, or irrigation districts. Powell hoped they would replace states or counties in regulating water, and since each district was self-sufficient in all natural resources, the struggle for water rights among settlers would be eliminated. This might have happened, and a new form of collectivism might have arisen, if, as Powell assumed, people had spread evenly throughout the arid region. He did not consider the dynamics of population, which usually operate unevenly. Once concentration of population occurred, then no geographical or political boundary was inviolate. In their aggressive search for water resources, settlers would have broken through the boundaries of his irrigation districts. Contrary to what he specifically insisted, canals have crossed mountains.[68] The disputes over water rights, characteristic of state and regional relations in the twentieth century, probably would have occurred, even if Powell had won. His plan required that an agrarian society remain in equilibrium, but the United States was a dynamic agroindustrial economy.

The pasturage district might have been a real force in western history. Originally (1878) Powell imagined cattlemen organizing to secure water through autonomous pasturage districts. When Powell reentered politics in 1888, he put the pasturage lands of the irrigation district under agricultural control, believing that in competition for land the farmers would win because they were willing to pay a higher price. If Powell had prevailed and if he had revived his idea of granting 2,560 acres in pasturage for each person and establishing local collective control of water resources, then the small rancher and homesteader might have become more dominant. In actuality the cattlemen with larger ambitions secured control of rangeland in amounts far beyond Powell's expectations. Recent students of land policy testify to the

68 U. S., Senate Report No. 1814, 50th Cong., 1st Sess., 122.

practicality of Powell's pasturage district concept, pointing to its incorporation in the Taylor Grazing Act of 1934, which allows local ranchers to exercise group control over grazing lands.[69]

Despite the abortive ending of the irrigation project and the following troubled period, the Geological Survey from this time on has always studied water location and use. The appraisal of underground and surface supply became an annual, if small, expense, first in the West and then a decade later in the entire country. Thus originated the water resources division of the modern Survey. In 1902, Congress gave the bureau responsibility for the new reclamation program. Powell's efforts remained an influence on future Survey work. F. H. Newell and A. P. Davis, who later played important roles in reclamation, said that Powell's knowledge and zeal were their first inspiration. Even the local boosters for irrigation, who disliked Powell for his emphatic statements about their limited water supply, after a while claimed him as their leader. When national planning became important during the Great Depression, Powell's influence was again remembered. Even though he had opposed control of reclamation by the national government, his concept of its responsibility was thoroughly modern.[70] The government was a powerful force because of the knowledge it acquired. Instinctively, it used this power in an intelligent, democratic way to advance the well-being of the common man, Powell felt. Twentieth-century planners have worshipped him for these ideas.

[69] E. Louise Peffer, *The Closing of the Public Domain: Disposal and Reservation Policies, 1900-1950* (Stanford, 1951), 24-25; Roy E. Huffman, *Irrigation Development and Public Water Policy* (New York, 1953), 123-24; H. L. Shantz, "History and Problems of Arid Lands Development," in *The Future of Arid Lands*, ed. Gilbert F. White (Washington, 1956), 18-19.

[70] When in committee, Allison and Hale pressed him by saying that only the government was capable of an all-round program, Powell conceded that "ultimately" it would say where the water "must be used." U. S., Senate Report No. 1466, 51st Cong., 1st Sess., 57.

Chapter Ten

INTERVAL OF DECLINE, 1892-1894

After the irrigation debacle the spirit and tempo of the Survey were transformed. Almost every year for a quarter of a century federal geologists and allied scientists had been introducing new and important research, either from scientific curiosity or because some public question arose which demanded authoritative knowledge. This expansive movement now faltered, as retaliatory action by western senators forced the bureau into a period of decline. In 1892, an election year, these hostile senators made an alliance against public science with those Cleveland Democrats who wanted a record of economy in Congress to demonstrate their fitness to govern. Republicans rallied to the defense of government science, thus producing the clearest partisan division in the history of the early Survey. The crushing result of the political warfare for the Survey was a 50 percent budget reduction. In 1892 the annual appropriation, which had risen to $800,000 in the late 1880's, fell below $400,000. After several years the danger of another sharp reduction passed. The diversified science of the Survey was a stabilizing force, and Powell's resignation in 1894 lessened considerably the congressional displeasure. Whoever the new director might be, there was likely to be a change in the emphasis of the Survey's science. The departure of Powell was the end of an era.

Clear public indication that the Survey was in trouble came during the budgetary discussion in the spring of 1891. Western senators, who the year before had had to restrain themselves lest they disrupt negotiations with the House of Representatives about the disposal of the irrigation survey, now could talk and act without inhibition. Senator Stewart made a savage speech against Powell and his "department," saying the director was "purely ornamental," and he headed "an army of dudes," who had spent $7 million and had done the West no good. He blamed the Survey for failure to get useful irrigation legislation.[1] Several senators, Stewart among them, slashed at the estimates, but this attack was parried, because Representative Cannon forced a compromise upon the conference committee, which limited the reduction to 10 or 15 percent.[2]

Paleontology was the vulnerable science of the Survey in 1892, in part because its study had grown so rapidly. Scientists in this field were a good example of what Powell advocated when in 1886 he called for a broad assault on human ignorance in the name of civilization. O. C. Marsh hoped through reassembling of the bones of extinct vertebrate species to illustrate and prove the theory of evolution. The studies by Lester Frank Ward of the flowering plants of the Mesozoic era and the collections by S. H. Scudder of fossil insects were justified because they indicated environmental conditions in past geological epochs. The Survey also did costly publishing for nonmembers, including three volumes by R. P. Whitfield on shellfish of the Cretaceous and Miocene strata in New Jersey. And it allowed J. S. Newberry to summarize his research of 30 years on the Paleozoic fish of North America. There was a flagrant abuse connected with the administration of paleontological studies, which stemmed from Powell's practice of granting heads of divisions broad discretionary powers. O. C. Marsh ran the division of vertebrate paleontology not as if he were in the government but as

[1] U. S., *Congressional Record*, 51st Cong., 2nd Sess., March 2, 1891, p. 3688.

[2] Arnold Hague to O. C. Marsh, March 7, 1891, U. S. Geological Survey, Hague Letter Books.

if he were collecting for Yale College or for himself. His discoveries, instead of being shipped to the National Museum in Washington, usually were retained in the storeroom of the college museum at New Haven, where they could be seen by only a few persons.[3] Suspicious and secretive by nature, Marsh sometimes hid the collections belonging to the government, or prohibited anyone from seeing them. Such conduct, extending over a decade, persuaded a number of scientists that Marsh hindered rather than advanced the study of paleontology in America.[4]

In the House appropriations committee, where government science first faced the crisis of 1892, Chairman W. S. Holman saved the budget of the Survey, which was not reduced even 10 percent. Arnold Hague noted that the Coast Survey and the National Museum were not let off as easily.[5] Then in May on the floor of the House Representative Herbert aroused the Democratic majority and successfully sponsored amendments which eliminated the items for salaries and research in paleon-

[3] H. F. Osborn to W. B. Allison, June 13, 1892, Copy, Marsh Papers. See, also, H. F. Osborn to W. B. Allison, May 26, June 8, 1892, H. F. Osborn Papers, American Museum of Natural History.

[4] W. B. Scott to O. C. Marsh, January 17, 1890, as printed in New York *Herald,* January 22, 1890, p. 5.

E. D. Cope had made a spectacular thrust in January 1890 when he peddled a statement of his feud with Marsh to the newspapers of New York City. The *Herald* bought the document and gave an unscrupulous reporter generous space and headlines. New York *Herald,* January 12, 13, 19, 20, 22, 26, 1890.

No doubt the newspaper succeeded in amusing its readers by making scientists look ridiculous, but the influence on the history of the Survey was slight. Cope's best opportunity had come during the upheaval of the first Cleveland administration; by 1890 his story was old stuff. "Scientific men are sick of it," Shaler said. New York *Herald,* January 13, 1890, p. 3.

Arnold Hague found that the articles in the *Herald* created far less excitement than he would have supposed; "no one in the Survey has spoken to me of the matter unless I first mentioned it," he told Marsh. Arnold Hague to O. C. Marsh, January 23, 1890, U. S. Geological Survey, Hague Letter Books.

Powell discounted the damage in Congress, and he was right. Trouble was beginning for him in January 1890, but not over paleontology.

[5] Arnold Hague to C. E. Dutton, March 26, 1892, U. S. Geological Survey, Hague Letter Books.

tology. The House was bound by repeated promises to reduce expenditures, Herbert said, and could begin fittingly with the Geological Survey. He quoted Agassiz' remark in 1885 that private individuals or societies would sponsor paleontology, and he complained that Marsh had twice published the same material on birds with teeth using government funds. Herbert incited other Democrats, among them Benton Mc-Millin of Tennessee, who won applause several times. Learning that Marsh had contributed financially to the publication of his research, McMillin denied that a great and powerful government should call upon a private citizen to make this sacrifice; "I am willing to relieve him . . . by cutting off the work in the future," he said. If money must be expended on the public lands of the United States, let it be spent for surveys which did the people some good, and not for "hunting up . . . the fossiliferous carcasses of those that were dead before the flood."[6]

When Herbert wanted to eliminate other parts of the appropriation, Republicans blocked him. One representative knew publications of the Survey were used in litigation over mining properties. Spokesmen from the Great Plains, keen on getting their share of the topographical mapping, expressed irritation at Herbert's proposed cut in that area. Every time, O. M. Kem of Nebraska said, a step was taken to help the farming class, somebody raised constitutional objections. Kem inspired cries of approval when he charged "a combination in this House against the Western wealth-producer."[7] At the end of a two-day discussion, H. H. Bingham, Republican from Philadelphia, turned to his Democratic colleagues and said that he wanted his people and the city where he lived to know that "your party, from every portion of this country" had been striking down scientific work of the government;

---

[6] U. S., *Congressional Record*, 52nd Cong., 1st Sess., May 19, 1892, p. 4436. See *ibid.*, May 18, 1892, p. 4377.

[7] *Ibid.*, May 18, 1892, p. 4399.

and only the "meager generosity of the gentleman from Indiana [Mr. Holman] and the solid vote of the Republican party" had saved the day. There were cheers from the Republican side.[8]

The conflict was renewed on the floor of the Senate after Powell had managed to have the items for paleontology restored to the Sundry Civil Bill by the committee on appropriations. W. F. Sanders, a Republican, defended the Survey in the name of science and progress, saying he doubted if the hostile senators were capable of "taking all these sciences into . . . [their] intellectual grasp," and determining the relative value of each.[9] He said it was easy to sacrifice science for economy's sake, telling the people nothing had been lost when, in fact, the progress of the nation had been arrested. Senator Stewart evoked laughter when he said scientists of the Survey were "tenderfeet," or young men on a vacation[10] and that not a mining man in the West took their opinions seriously. Powell's learning was the wrong kind; he knew too well the geology of Congress; he knew how to bleed the Treasury, how "to hire admirers," and "fool the people." Dawes replied that Stewart never mentioned extravagant and useless expenditure "until he thought one way should be adopted to irrigate the arid lands and the distinguished Director of the Geological Survey thought another way was wiser." Some senators complained that the timing was wrong for major decisions about government science. "We never hear of the Geological Survey," E. O. Wolcott of Colorado said, until the budget was reported in.[11] Then if senators objected, they were accused of blocking an important money bill or delaying adjournment. Sanders was among those who thought it unfortunate that whenever an appropriation bill was considered, the merit of the Survey or "the action, wisdom, and adoration of the

8 *Ibid.*, May 19, 1892, p. 4437.
9 *Ibid.*, July 14, 1892, p. 6157.
10 *Ibid.*, July 8, 1892, pp. 5888-89.
11 *Ibid.*, 6151.

Director" entered the discussion.[12] These issues should be set-tled by independent legislation, he said.

The absence of an aggressive and knowledgeable floor leader in the Senate gravely handicapped Powell and the Survey. Allison, once head of the joint commission and long-time chairman of the committee on appropriations, was demor-alized by another attack on Marsh. This time it came from H. F. Osborn, a vertebrate paleontologist, who recently had become associated with the American Museum of Natural History in New York City. Wanting to build up the museum's collections, Osborn planned to exploit the extraordinary dino-saur remains in Converse County, Wyoming. Marsh already was there, and he tried to prevent Osborn from collecting in this rich locality by claiming everything for the government.[13] Osborn, who also had been barred from Survey fossils in New Haven, was impatient with the argument that there was no room for them in Washington. Had any real effort been made to house them in Washington? he asked. He told Allison that Marsh's interest, vertebrate paleontology, was not as essential as invertebrate studies to the progress of the Survey, being "of a less practical and of a more purely scientific character."[14] Allison made the feeble statement to his colleagues that Marsh's work was speculative and that Powell believed it to be important.[15]

Initially, the voting favored the Survey. On July 8 there were three roll call votes on Herbert's amendments taking paleontology out of the Survey. Each time the Republican majority stood behind the committee on appropriations, although Stewart, Wolcott, and half a dozen other members of the party voted with the Democrats.[16] All the Republican rebels came from beyond the Great Plains. Six days later, on

12 *Ibid.*, July 8, 1892, p. 5887.
13 O. C. Marsh to J. W. Powell, March 14, 1892, Copy, Marsh Papers.
14 H. F. Osborn to W. B. Allison, June 13, 1892, Copy, *ibid.*
15 U. S., *Congressional Record*, 52nd Cong., 1st Sess., July 8, 1892, p. 5891.
16 *Ibid.*, 5892-93. The three results were scored as 31-21, 29-18, and 27-21.

July 14, Powell's enemies were more successful. First, Senator Wolcott of Colorado proposed an indiscriminate reduction of $150,000, which failed despite the support of four or five Republican senators, who came from no particular geographical area. Then J. M. Carey of Wyoming introduced a selective reduction of $200,000, specifying deletions in both the paleontology and geology programs, but making no significant change in the outlay for topographical mapping. The movement of the Republicans away from the recommendations of the committee accelerated as senators from Maine, Michigan, Wyoming, and Washington joined the opposition, more than offsetting several Democratic votes which went the other way. On two roll calls the Carey amendment was approved.[17]

When the New York *Times* of July 15 reported the "successful revolt" against Powell's "autocratic sway," it warned its readers that the battle could still be lost.[18] The director was as strong in the House as Commissioner R. P. Porter of the Census Bureau, and Holman, chairman of the committee on appropriations, would never desert the Survey, as long as his son remained an employee. But the opportunity to maneuver behind the scenes was soon cut off. As the *Times* predicted, Holman's committee did recommend nonconcurrence when the Sundry Civil Bill was returned from the Senate on July 19. If this recommendation had been approved, the disputed items would have gone to conference committee, which so often in the past the director had used to his advantage. When, however, J. H. Bankhead of Alabama moved to accept the senatorial figures, Holman was not allowed to speak under a rule requiring unanimous consent, and by a vote of 94 to 25 the chamber accepted Carey's amendment.[19]

17 *Ibid.*, July 14, 1892, pp. 6154, 6158, 6161. The three tabulations, with the anti-Survey forces scored first, were 24-28, 26-23, 28-25.
18 New York *Times*, July 15, 1892, p. 5.
19 While the Senate debated in July, there circulated in Washington a pamphlet written by Jules Marcou entitled *The Geological Map of the United States and the United States Geological Survey* (1892). Marcou

The leading scientific bureau of the government now suffered the consequences of the congressional reduction. Only a remnant of the paleontology program could be maintained —six persons out of 28, or one division. Marsh and Scudder were among the many to leave the Survey.[20] In geology Congress had abolished three of the five positions at $4,000 a year, which had been attractive for scientists. The Survey released Emmons, Becker, and Pumpelly. In other changes, Gilbert and Bailey Willis accepted smaller salaries, T. Nelson Dale moved to Williams College, and Van Hise took a professorship at the University of Wisconsin.[21] The number of temporary and per diem positions increased, and four of the younger geologists (Cross, Darton, Lindgren, and Weed) learned they would soon be asked to resign.[22] Fortunately, these letters of resignation were recalled after a month, but they contributed to the deep sense of crisis which pervaded all branches and

disliked most of the developments in American geology since the 1840's. He was partial to the term "taconic" as descriptive of a large category of native rock, and he did not consider physical geology a serious branch of the discipline. Nor did he welcome the diversity of scientific endeavor within the Geological Survey, which should do only stratigraphic geology. These prejudices went into the pamphlet, along with critical or savage commentary on Director Powell and the heads of divisions. In another and shorter pamphlet issued later in 1892, bearing the title *A Little More Light on the United States Geological Survey*, Marcou said that his first pamphlet influenced the action taken against the Geological Survey in the Senate. And the *American Geologist* made the same assertion. This influence is not apparent in the senatorial discussion.

[20] C. D. Walcott to O. C. Marsh, August 12, 1892, Marsh Papers.

Early in August, F. W. Clarke, chief of the division of chemistry, reported the resignation of four scientists and the reduction of the work to the simplest terms. F. W. Clarke to J. W. Powell, August 8, 1892, U. S. Geological Survey, Letters Received, 1892.

[21] J. W. Powell to the Secretary of the Interior, August 13, 1892, to G. F. Becker, to S. F. Emmons, and to Raphael Pumpelly, August 6, 1892, U. S. Geological Survey, Letters Sent, 1892. T. N. Dale to J. W. Powell, August 17, 1892, *ibid.*, Letters Received, 1892. Arnold Hague to O. C. Marsh, July 20, 1892, to W. H. Weed, August 17, 1892, U. S. Geological Survey, Hague Letter Books.

[22] J. W. Powell to C. W. Cross, to N. H. Darton, to Waldemar Lindgren, and to W. H. Weed, August 6, 1892, U. S. Geological Survey, Letters Sent, 1892. *Ibid.*, September 15, 1892.

ranks. Another threatening possibility was a congressional investigation. Just before adjournment in late July, the Senate authorized appointment of a committee to investigate the Survey. Senator Wolcott of Colorado was the chairman, and Carey of Wyoming was another member. They promised to begin after the election.

The director himself was a pitiful figure, fallen from the position of power he once had held. Stupefied by the congressional action, he became "unfit" to do anything, "which necessitated recalling matters, or planning for the future."[23] He relied more and more on C. D. Walcott and went away in September, leaving his chief paleontologist "full power to do what he pleased."[24] Although he returned to Washington in the middle of December, he still did not take charge. This apathy continued into the new year. Becker confided to his mother that Powell must retire if the Survey was to survive; otherwise both would be smashed.[25] Paleontologist Walcott also speculated about the directorship when he explained to Van Hise the strong feeling in both the House and Senate against Powell. The legislators were convinced that Powell used political methods in obtaining appropriations, that he had been extravagant in spending, and that he had not dealt fairly with the scientific men of the country, particularly the vertebrate paleontologists.[26]

At the beginning of 1893 when the future seemed darkest, the forces against the Survey suddenly lost their drive. Chairman Wolcott of the senatorial committee tried to divert the investigation by making a speech in the Senate against the Survey and by again moving to reduce its budget. The senator wanted to restore the bureau of mines and mining of 1879. Evidently he was advised in his purpose by a geologist intimately acquainted with the history of the Survey, for he knew that Gilbert had begun a study of the moon, which he

---

23 C. D. Walcott to O. C. Marsh, October 12, 1892, Marsh Papers.
24 Notes in the Emmons Papers, Box 30.
25 G. F. Becker to S. C. T. Becker, July 10, 1892, Becker Papers.
26 C. D. Walcott to C. R. Van Hise, December 10, 1892, Van Hise Papers.

ridiculed, and he could see that the geological mapping was
going to take longer and cost more than Powell had claimed
in the 1880's. One of the weapons Wolcott used was an editorial in *Natural Science,* a new English magazine, which
both praised and criticized the Survey. Omitting the laudatory
comments, Wolcott quoted the editorial as saying a geological
survey was a commercial investment. A nation must ask what
progress had been made in the preparation of the geological
maps and the value of the maps for improved economic life.
In other words, the duty of a survey was to survey, and its
output in maps indicated whether a nation was getting its
money's worth. Judged in these terms, the Geological Survey
fell short of reasonable expectations, for despite the many
valuable maps on special subjects, only one sheet of the general geological map had appeared. The editorial charged unnecessary extravagance in secondary matters, reading, "We
have received such a plethora of illustrations of Pleistocene
scenery and Dismal Swamps, that one has been tempted to
exclaim, 'This is magnificent, but it is not geology.' "[27]
Wolcott assured his colleagues that they were competent to
restore the original Survey. "We may be dazed by scientific
terms," he said, ". . . we may not be alive to the distinctions
between the upper and the lower carboniferous, or the difference between the cenozoic and mesozoic ages; but we are
able to direct an intelligent investigation of the regions of
this great country which give promise of rich deposits."[28]

The Senate was not impressed by the best speech ever made
against the Survey. Wolcott had been sent out as chairman of
a committee to investigate the bureau; now he was back without a report, attacking what he had been commissioned to
study. Blackburn of Kentucky thought such a procedure unfair to both the Senate and the Survey. Gorman of Maryland,
insisting that the legislature had neither the time nor the

27 "The Crisis in the United States Geological Survey," *Natural Science,*
I (1892), 644-45.
28 U. S., *Congressional Record,* 52nd Cong., 2nd Sess., February 20, 1893,
p. 1844.

information to make so "radical an innovation," called for a thorough examination and if it proved to be in the interest of the government "to abolish the whole system," then he would be glad to so vote.[29] Call and Manderson thought Wolcott's idea of a geological survey was unreasonably narrow, catering too much to the metallic mining industry. Why shouldn't the phosphates of the state of Florida benefit from scientific exploration? Call asked. Manderson argued that those parts of the country without mineral wealth deserved consideration. His state of Nebraska needed a topographical survey, and "it is our right to have it."[30] Three-fourths of Kansas had been mapped, but practically none of Nebraska, he complained. Apparently the four senators were expressing majority sentiment, because on February 20, 1893, Wolcott's motion to reduce topographical mapping by $100,000 was defeated, 37-18, and later in the year Congress approved a budget like the one in 1892.

When congressional pressure was relaxed, Powell resigned the directorship with dignity. His health improving, he wrote 100 pages of the annual report for 1892-1893, which summed up the scientific accomplishments of the Survey since its founding. In autumn of 1893 he felt strong enough to attend an irrigation congress in Los Angeles, where he created an uproar among the delegates by generalizing about the greed of corporations and the enormity of speculation in western lands.[31] At the end of the year he was said to be administering the directorship vigorously. The occasion for leaving the Survey was genuine: he needed an operation to lessen the pain of his old wound from Shiloh. In May 1894 some 70 newspapers reported the resignation; many of them provided the name of the new director, C. D. Walcott, chosen by Powell.[32]

29 *Ibid.*, 1850.

30 *Ibid.*, 1848.

31 F. H. Newell to H. C. Rizer, October 14, 1893, U. S. Geological Survey, Letters Received, 1893.

32 Powell was still director of the Bureau of Ethnology.

King was the founder of the Survey, but Powell was its great organizer. He brought to the directorship the same bold and fertile mind which had inspired his own research in the Colorado River region. His practice of allowing the heads of divisions to pursue freely their scientific interests, led to many centers of independent research within the Survey. Powell's phenomenal success in securing money from Congress was based primarily on the confidence powerful congressional committees placed in him. Their understanding of science was not profound, but the legislators knew the director's past record as a farmer in Illinois, a Union soldier severely wounded in battle, and a sensational explorer. They observed him play the roles of authoritative scientist, persuasive teacher, and satisfactory spoilsman, and they came to trust him implicitly. The work of the topographical division revealed Powell's temperament at its best and worst. By pushing ahead on his own authority, he had scientific knowledge ready when the demand rose; northeastern urban interests saw uses for topographical maps as soon as they were published. At the same time he was so intent on completing the national map that he sacrificed scientific accuracy in its preparation. During the irrigation survey he seemed ready to ignore or undermine the science of civil engineering so that he could apply his topographical maps. Ideologically, Powell was doctrinaire. He wanted to submit the arid West to a novel and rigid socioeconomic pattern, and in trying to do this he pushed far beyond the range of popular or representative thinking. For this antidemocratic rashness he suffered severely.

Even though he was forced out of the directorship because of his land policies, Powell retains an impressive position in the history of American public science. He raised government expenditures for science to new high levels and inspired research in many fields of knowledge. His alliances in Congress gave him great political power. He belongs in the company of that distinguished group of nineteenth-century scientist-administrators, such as Joseph Henry of the Smithsonian, A. D. Bache of the Coast Survey, Rear Admiral C. H. Davis, and Colonel J. J. Abert of the Topographical Corps of Engineers.

The Geological Survey was the leading scientific bureau of the post-Civil War period and was the government's most productive research agency during the nineteenth century. It had the advantage of a dual organization, wielding the power of the government bureau, yet enjoying the freedom of the scientific society.[33] It used this advantage to make geology and paleontology the primary research sciences in the United States after 1865. Political stability came through the services to groups outside the government, where the Survey found an ideal ally in the mining industry which was driving the American economy ahead during the second half of the nineteenth century. Other connections in the North, South, and West gave the bureau a broad base for its political strength, enabling it to withstand reaction better when it came. The success of the Geological Survey attracted the attention of public spokesmen for agriculture, who sought to organize federal research on a comparative scale in behalf of their interest. They succeeded within the Department of Agriculture after 1900.

The Survey brought post-Darwinian science into the government, informing the nation-state of the latest European and American developments. It represented a new breed of public scientist, impatient at the "slower past,"[34] fertile with plans for research to consume many lifetimes, and so fiercely competitive among themselves that the quest for knowledge was often transformed into a passion to monopolize it.

33 *Nature,* XLIX (1894), 434-36.
34 U.S.G.S. *First Annual Report,* 75.

Chapter Eleven

EPILOGUE: THE SURVEY
IN THE TWENTIETH CENTURY

There are good reasons for not continuing intensively with the story of the Survey into the twentieth century. The tensions of the nineteenth-century Survey, which make it so attractive for study, drop sharply as the modern period begins. The bureau and its purposes cease to dominate the relations of science and government on the national scene; the massive confrontations with Congress do not recur; the crisis atmosphere, chronic with geological surveys since the Civil War, vanishes. Another factor which almost precludes original research is the dwindling of the Survey records just before the turn of the century. Between 1900 and the beginning of World War I they do not exist at all. For some branches of the bureau this lack extends into the 1920's; a legal and thorough destruction was carried out during the directorship of George Otis Smith, Walcott's successor. What particularly handicaps the historian is the absence of letters received and sent; without them he cannot examine accurately and closely intra-Survey relations and congressional events.

But there still is the opportunity, indeed even the need, to generalize about the twentieth-century Survey. Knowledge of its broad features after Powell had resigned lends perspective to his directorship. Inevitably some of his policies were abandoned as the bureau struggled to rise again in government circles, and this development adds to our total picture. A view of the twentieth century also allows for continuity. We may learn how much the formative period, examined in this volume, shaped the later course of the institution. Finally, attention to the twentieth century will bring knowledge of the new directions which the Survey has taken, of the contemporary situations favorable and unfavorable to its progress, and of the part it has played in our time when the tempo and scope of government science have increased so radically.

Director Walcott rehabilitated the Survey; he brought it back from the disasters under Powell by emphasizing the science projects which were not subject to criticism in Congress or enjoyed manifest public support. Economic geology again became primary.[1] Emmons returned and took command of the section of metalliferous ores. First revisiting Leadville, he then went to Aspen, Colorado, in 1895, where miners had urged an investigation four years before. Walcott sent Whitman Cross to Cripple Creek in the same state. Freed of the former restrictions upon his activity, Emmons soon was submitting plans for studies of the metallic minerals in half a dozen states of the Far West. The demand for Survey mineral science came from new quarters when the gold rush to Alaska began in 1898, and during the next decade practically every mining camp in that vast territory was visited or investigated by bureau geologists. The new director intensified research in the geology of nonmetalliferous deposits, which were a source of fuels and fertilizers. The coal age in the national economy was coming to a climax, and many Americans wanted to be sure that the nation had sufficient coal reserves. Walcott stressed studies in the western coalfields, and he also supervised nine reports on oil. Later in the twentieth century, oil shales would be examined closely, and an earnest and successful search made for potash (a fertilizer) in west Texas and eastern New Mexico. The director always reported confidently on mineral statistics, collected in the twentieth century by a

1 U.S.G.S. *Sixteenth Annual Report,* 7.

division of mining and mineral resources. Returning prosperity after the depression of the 1890's had lifted the value of mineral production into the billions of dollars; and producers everywhere desired information about the "wonderful industrial activity."[2] By a resolution Congress had shown its approval of this division, which was also involved with technology. In 1905 offices were opened in Denver, Salt Lake City, and San Francisco. Neither statistical nor technological work were to remain a permanent part of the Survey. In 1910 mining technology became part of the original Bureau of Mines, and in 1925 the collection of production information was transferred there.

Walcott engaged the Survey heavily in the examination of water resources—measuring streams, locating and appraising underground waters and artesian wells, and studying geologically the structure and permeability of the water-bearing rocks. In this division or branch he used some of his most talented employees. F. H. Newell, who had survived the elimination of the irrigation survey, was head; Gilbert, Leverett, Darton, and R. T. Hill were four geologists asked to make reports. A. P. Davis and W. D. Johnson joined from the topographical corps. Congress soon doubled the money, and a new publication series (the water supply papers) appeared. Several discoveries in the field dramatized the value and effectiveness of the work. At Rocky Ford in eastern Colorado, Gilbert predicted that an artesian source of water would be found below the surface between 735 and 1,135 feet. In all probability, he added, this water horizon lay less than 1,000 feet down. Within a year the Santa Fé railroad reported that a supply of 80 gallons per minute had been found at a depth of 790 feet. At Quitman, Georgia, the question arose as to whether or not the use of an underground channel to dispose of sewage would contaminate the wells of the town.

2 U.S.G.S. *Twenty-first Annual Report,* 102.

Survey hydrographers convinced the community that the contamination would occur by introducing a large amount of salt into one of the wells leading to the underground channel and then finding traces of salt in the other wells. The sewage, the scientists argued, would penetrate as the salt had done. In 1902 Congress declared that the Reclamation Service, founded that year, belonged in the Geological Survey, but this construction activity was never fully integrated into the regular organization. In 1907 Newell assumed charge of a completely independent bureau for reclamation.

Topography was Walcott's most critical problem, considering the professional and personal issues at stake. The director struck a blow for scientific integrity when he announced that the quality of the topographic maps must be improved. He established the office of editor of topographic maps, first occupied by Marcus Baker, to help insure this quality. In the field, mapping on the small scale of four miles to the inch was eliminated, greater care was taken in sketching topography, and the Coast Survey method for running the more important horizontal lines (leveling) was adopted. Walcott also gave notice that he was not going to use the lower positions of the topographic branch as patronage for Congress. He placed all members in the classified service, thus limiting "appointments to men whose qualifications have been tested by an impartial and thorough examination."[3] These changes hurt mostly the two men whom Powell had raised to supreme command, Henry Gannett and A. H. Thompson. Gannett was chief geographer, and for years Thompson had directed the topographical work beyond the one hundredth meridian. Walcott removed both officials (although they stayed in the Survey) and assumed himself the leadership of that branch. The office of chief geographer was vacant as long as he remained director.

[3] U.S.G.S. *Sixteenth Annual Report,* 8.

The new opportunity for topography came in 1897 when Congress ordered the Survey to map the public forest reservations which had begun to accumulate under the Act of March 3, 1891. For many years the annual reports carried extensive accounts of this topographical work in the western forests. Seeing an educational benefit in good topographic maps, Walcott secured congressional authorization to sell them directly to the public, which Massachusetts had been doing since the 1880's with the maps which had been made there under the cooperative agreement.

A cautious and conciliatory atmosphere now prevailed within the Survey. The long Republican rule, beginning with McKinley in 1897, lessened the threat from economy-minded Democrats, and when the Democratic party returned to power in 1913 under Wilson there was no renewal of the hostility toward public science, which had been shown in Cleveland's time. Walcott made no complaints about paleontology, year after year accepting from Congress the same low appropriation for this once important and controversial science. Marsh again worked for the Survey, and after Marsh's death in 1899 Osborn became chief paleontologist for a brief period. With Walcott new duties were not the prelude to ideological or bureaucratic struggle. When the Survey assumed the mapping of the national forests, it also agreed to specify the value, amount, and kind of timber, and to make plans for its care and maintenance. For this purpose a division of forestry was established with Gannett appointed head. But Gannett was not aggressive like Gifford Pinchot, the government's chief forester. Pinchot boasted that he sometimes changed the boundaries of forest reserves as they had been laboriously mapped by the Geological Survey. And in 1905 without protest from either Walcott or Gannett he brought the Survey's resource management into the Forest Service within the Department of Agriculture.

Sometimes, however, Walcott could be as insistent and

unyielding as Powell. In 1906 he wrote to J. C. Branner, who having served as state geologist of Arkansas in the 1890's was now a professor at Stanford University and also held an appointment in the Geological Survey for part-time work. Walcott proposed that Branner make available his materials on Arkansas coalfields so that the regular geologists could study them more fully. Branner replied that he would do the resurvey for the national bureau, but Walcott refused, saying that his geologists were about to enter the field in Arkansas. After this Branner resigned his position in the Survey, published his correspondence with Walcott in the magazine *Science,* characterized the proposal to enter Arkansas as "an outrage," and concluded that the attitude of Walcott toward state geologists and university faculty was "intolerable."[4] Both men accused the other of poor science.

But the trend toward collaboration was too powerful to be diverted by personal misunderstandings. At a meeting of state geologists later in 1906 Walcott pledged his support to fuller cooperation. In his first annual report George Otis Smith, the new director after Walcott resigned to become secretary of the Smithsonian Institution, made favorable reference to a two-day conference in 1907, attended by members of state surveys and division heads of the federal bureau, where mutual problems were discussed exhaustively. By the 1920's the states were contributing three-quarters of a million dollars to Survey science, not only in geology and topography, but also in stream gauging and mineral statistics.

Smith's accession to the directorship in 1907 coincided with one of the political climaxes of the Progressive Era. As Smith came to power, both the executive and legislative branches of the federal government were initiating programs to conserve or utilize more effectively the natural resources of

4 *Science,* New Series, XXIV (July-December, 1906), 532-37, 692-93, 722-28.

the public domain. The primary contribution of the Survey was scientific classification; the bureau designated the coal lands and segregated other properties valuable for oil, gas, phosphate, potash, water power, and reservoir sites. Then the public land laws of Congress could be more soundly administered and the conservation policies of the President implemented. For several decades the land classification or conservation branch of the Survey was a major concern.

An early and influential event in Smith's directorship was World War I, which temporarily transformed the duties of the Survey. In the beginning the American position as a neutral nation caused the bureau to inquire whether the United States could support itself independently in minerals crucial to the national economy. By 1916 the range of study was narrowing, as the Council of National Defense began asking for information about war minerals; the same year the topographers organized a division of military surveys. When war came in 1917, the Survey sought new mineral deposits for munitions manufacturing and made a national inventory of mineral wealth. All the topographers either joined the U.S. Army or worked on War Department projects. Resource appraisal soon had a worldwide significance. In 1918 the Survey made an agreement with President Wilson's Inquiry, a group of experts assembled to advise him concerning the peace conference. Under this agreement the bureau constructed a world atlas, showing the production of important mineral commodities in various areas. After completing the atlas the Survey continued on its own to study foreign mineral deposits.

Smith was director for almost 25 years, from 1907 to 1930, and this long term makes a convenient framework for further generalizations about the course of the Survey in the twentieth century. At a time when rapid change at home and abroad was drawing the federal government more and more into the national life, the Survey was a bureau in Washington under which new ideas and programs in science could be initiated. After a period of trial these programs could be given an independent position in the federal establishment. It was also during Smith's directorship, however, that scientists expressed resentment at the slow growth of the Survey and the restricted range of its intellectual activity. In 1898 Walcott had announced with pride a budget of $1 million, more than double what it had been at the nadir of Powell's regime only four years before. Thereafter improvement was very gradual, and 30 years would pass before the $2-million mark was reached in the fiscal year 1928-1929 at the end of Smith's tenure. This slow advance frustrated the completion of the large, important, and cherished project—the national topographic map, which despite Powell's departure had not been forgotten. Even worse, the bureau could not keep many of its talented scientists; better offers from industry or universities caused a steady loss of Survey personnel which intensified during the inflation after World War I, when under the circumstances of an inflexible budget and a soaring cost of living, the coal, oil, and metal sections were almost wiped out. In 1921 nearly 70 manuscripts lay unpublished because of lack of funds.

Criticism of the Survey's research went along with the institutional problems. In 1912 C. R. Van Hise, the Wisconsin geologist, called the Survey "a department of practical geology," which was not "contributing in any large way to the advancement of science." Under King and Powell, he said, the Survey had been "the center of the world" for the advancement of science. W. H. Hobbs of the University of Michigan, who published in the bulletins and annual reports, agreed with Van Hise that there was "no justification for the almost complete neglect of work in pure science which has been characteristic of later administrations."[5]

Answering these charges, officials admitted and defended

5 *Ibid.*, XXXVI (July-December, 1912), 196, 478.

the change in emphasis of Survey science. Smith said the research conducted under government auspices should be "largely practical."[6] A. H. Brooks, head of the Alaskan branch, constructed charts to show that in 1890 less than one percent of Survey publications involved applied geology; in 1910, 98 percent of the publications were in this field. Defending the transformation, Brooks insisted that the people must be the final arbiters as to what phase of science was to be emphasized. He believed that they wanted practical geology. Neither Brooks nor Smith would identify himself exclusively with practical geology. Brooks saw "a grave danger that, carried away by the present furor for practical results, we may lose sight of our scientific ideals."[7] Smith listed Survey studies and topics which lay outside practical geology. He included ore deposits and theories as to their origin, knowing that in 1900 Van Hise himself had participated in an exciting discussion of ore-formation theory with two of his colleagues, Emmons and Waldemar Lindgren, speaking before the American Institute of Mining Engineers. This reading of papers marked Lindgren's rise to leadership among mining geologists. He left the Survey in 1912 for the Massachusetts Institute of Technology, having learned and published a fantastic amount on the science of ore deposition.

Subsequently, Smith joined his critics in complaining about the unhealthy condition of Survey research. As his long tenure approached its end, he became very outspoken. In 1928 he pointed out that there could be no applied science unless there was science to apply. The next year he grumbled about the undue proportion of energies in the geologic branch going to applied geology; too little of those energies, he added, were directed toward the search for unknown general relations and laws. Experience during World War I had disillusioned him about popular will as a guide to distribution of

6 *Ibid.*, 402.
7 *Ibid.*, 477.

research effort. Businessmen came to Washington in large numbers to rub shoulders with government scientists, but Smith was not sure that this important segment of the popular will really understood what research was. He noted a "tendency to order a piece of research by telegraph for delivery next day."[8]

A brighter prospect seemed near in 1931 when Walter C. Mendenhall, Smith's successor as director, persuaded Congress to make a special appropriation of $100,000 for fundamental research in geologic science. The next year (1932) he reported that the Survey budget had risen to $3 million, only four years after it had reached $2 million. But then came the New Deal, which may have submerged the policy of basic research. Again, as in the Progressive Era, an enlarged government needed scientists, this time to serve in public works projects. These emergency activities tended to replace the usual Survey work, which was described by Director Mendenhall in 1935 as "at a low ebb"; the geologic branch had suffered almost a 40 percent reduction.[9]

After the Great Depression came the decades of war and their revolutionary effect on the position of science in the federal government. In 1939 the Survey began again to stress strategic minerals, and during the next 20 years broad programs were developed in the search for fissionable materials (geology) and in the task of informing the armed forces about "terrane conditions" (topography).[10] The budget increased tremendously; $67 million was appropriated directly by Congress for the fiscal year ending in 1965. But there was still the need to argue for basic research. During the Korean War Director William E. Wrather said that the Survey should be allowed

8 *Forty-seventh Annual Report of the Director of the U.S. Geological Survey, 1925-26* (Washington, 1926), 30.

9 *Annual Report of the Secretary of the Interior for the Fiscal Year Ended June 30, 1935* (Washington, 1935), 233.

10 *Annual Report of the Secretary of the Interior for the Fiscal Year Ended June 30, 1956* (Washington, 1956), 107.

to continue its "carefully planned research and geologic mapping"; technical advances and a high standard of living, Director Wrather said, were "the by-products of scientific research carried on for its own sake, and with no specific objectives other than the desire to learn fundamental truths about natural phenomena."[11] By the 1960's pleas for fundamental research had disappeared from the annual reports; perhaps it was assumed that Survey programs would give both practical results and new knowledge. One evidence of improved standing was the serious return to an old and often frustrated purpose: in 1963 Director Thomas B. Nolan announced a plan to complete the mapping of the United States by 1981.[12] This would come almost exactly 100 years after Powell had begun the job in 1882 by ordering his topographers south into the Appalachian highlands.

[11] *Annual Report of the Secretary of the Interior for the Fiscal Year Ended June 30, 1952* (Washington, 1952), 219, 223.

[12] *Annual Report of the Secretary of the Interior for the Fiscal Year Ending June 30, 1963* (Washington, 1963), 383.

NOTE ON SOURCES

1. *Documents and Personal Papers*

The National Archives was the indispensable depository; without its collections many pages of this book could not have been written. There are materials on all four scientific surveys after 1865, either in the records of the Department of War or the Department of the Interior. The incoming correspondence from King and Wheeler are part of the records of the Office of the Chief of Engineers, Department of War. Some of this correspondence could not be found. For King at least this was not a handicap, because when the Exploration of the Fortieth Parallel was completed, he had most of his letters and reports to General Humphreys copied into a leather-bound volume, which is part of the records of the Department of the Interior. The materials on the Powell survey are letters received and press copies of the letters sent, mainly from the period after 1875. Hayden's records lack a solid core of letters sent. Beginning with the Geological Survey proper in 1879, the records become bulkier. During this period, the letters sent by the director were transcribed with pen and ink from the press copies into oversize volumes.

The O. C. Marsh Papers in the Peabody Museum of Natural History, Yale University, were the most valuable personal collection. Marsh's high and controversial positions in both the Geological Survey and the National Academy of Sciences encouraged correspondence. Usually, he did not make a copy of his outgoing letters. Collections of several other geologists of the Survey in the Library of Congress were consulted. The G. F. Becker Papers provided informative letters to his mother and from his friend, S. F. Emmons. In the Emmons Papers, a diary and later account of the diamond fraud dispel several legends about that famous incident. Both these sources reflect the dissatisfaction of one group within the Survey. On the other hand, the friends and defenders of Powell are revealed in the W J McGee Papers, which contain both the incoming correspondence and copies of the outgoing. The letter books of Arnold Hague in the National Archives, which have copies of hundreds of his letters sent, fall into neither the critical nor the apologetic category. If status were the criterion, then Hague belonged to the Emmons and Becker faction. Actually, he formed an alliance with Powell, based on their common interest in Yellowstone National Park. Hague's descriptions of important and intimate scenes in the history of the Survey attain great objectivity. His letter books were exceedingly helpful for the chapter on Yellowstone Park.

Some personal papers were useful for one issue or event: the diary of Alexander Winchell in the Michigan State Historical Society, describing the struggle between King and Hayden for the directorship; a few letters by King from the Carl Schurz collection in the Library of Congress (for the early months of the Geological Survey in 1879); and the correspondence with and concerning O. C. Marsh in the H. F. Osborn Papers of the American Museum of Natural History. Through microfilm I examined the Rutherford B. Hayes Papers in Fremont, Ohio, the W. M. Stewart letter books in the Nevada State Historical Society, and the Clarence King section of the James D. Hague Papers in the Huntington Library. In this Huntington Library source there are less than 100 pieces from King's two years with the Geological Survey. Before 1879, his letters deal primarily with business affairs.

Other collections were not seen enough to permit an all-round characterization, but they should be mentioned because of their intrinsic importance. The Papers of Simon Newcomb in the Library of Congress reveal the reaction of persons outside Washington to events in the nation's capital. The letters received by Alexander Agassiz make a row of file cases in the

Museum of Comparative Zoology at Harvard College; the copies of letters sent are less plentiful. The incoming letters in the Joseph Leidy Papers of the Academy of Natural Sciences of Philadelphia and similar correspondence in the James Hall Papers of the New York State Museum at Albany should always be helpful to historians of nineteenth-century American science.

2. *Government Publications*

The four western surveys and the permanent bureau published several hundred volumes. In 1904 L. F. Schmeckebier prepared a *Catalogue and Index of the Publications of the Hayden, King, Powell, and Wheeler Surveys,* which appeared as Geological Survey Bulletin No. 222. The *Annual Reports* of the Geological Survey for the period of this study are thick volumes of quarto size, offering advanced and detailed scientific knowledge. They contain also nature description, elementary geology, and speculation on the deeper meaning of physical events. For the *Tenth, Eleventh, Twelfth, and Thirteenth Annual Reports* there are additional volumes on irrigation, including the important testimony by Powell before the committee on irrigation of the House of Representatives in 1890, *Eleventh Annual Report of the U. S. Geological Survey, 1889-1890,* Part II, *Irrigation,* 203-89. King projected the *Monographs* of the Geological Survey as learned treatises on economic and general geology. Powell did not disturb this plan; rather he grafted on to it a project for equally large and learned works in paleontology. He also instituted the *Bulletins,* which allowed for shorter articles on geology, paleontology, topography, chemistry, physics, and bibliography. A series of *Reports on Mineral Resources* first appeared in 1882, and at the end of Powell's regime the *Folios of the Geologic Atlas* were issued. From time to time the Geological Survey brings out a booklet listing its publications since 1879, including the categories in this paragraph.

The *Congressional Record* with its wide pages, double columns, and small print has been searched closely. For the five years, 1879, 1886, 1888, 1890, and 1892, the materials are very full.

The reports of the House and Senate can be the finest expression of Congress' investigating and legislating powers, and several times during the history of the Survey these reports approached the ideal. U. S., House Report No. 612, 43rd Cong., 1st Sess., published the hearings and findings of the committee on the public lands in 1874. Four years later the House addressed the executive branch for more information, and the respective replies of Powell, Hayden, and Humphreys, U. S., House Ex. Docs. No. 80, No. 81, and No. 88, 45th Cong., 2nd Sess., gave many useful facts and statistics. The decisive report of the National Academy of Sciences and accompanying letters of the chief protagonists constitute U. S., House Misc. Doc. No. 5, 45th Cong., 3rd Sess. The next group of documents originated during the congressional investigation from 1884 to 1886. U. S., Senate Misc. Doc. No. 82, 49th Cong., 1st Sess., is the testimony before the joint commission. Chapter VII draws heavily upon the 1,100-page transcript of this hearing; the report is also an almanac on the Geological Survey. The important recommendations of the majority are in U. S., House Report No. 2740, 49th Cong., 1st Sess.; the minority speak in this document and also in U. S., House Report No. 2214, 49th Cong., 1st Sess. For the story of Yellowstone Park, U. S., House Report No. 1386, 53rd Cong., 2nd Sess., is one of the best sources. *The Early History of Yellowstone National Park and its Relation to National Park Policies* (Washington, 1932) by L. C. Cramton also was helpful. Cramton listed the bills and debates affecting the Yellowstone country for each Congress from the 42nd to the 54th. Ironically, he missed the most important speech: S. S. Cox's in December 1886 (U. S., *Congressional Record*, 49th Cong., 2nd Sess., 151, 153). In U. S., Senate Report No. 1814, 50th Cong., 1st Sess., and in

U. S., Senate Report No. 2613, 50th Cong., 2nd Sess., both of which are hearings before the committee on appropriations, Powell unfolds his plan to encourage irrigation in the arid West. U. S., Senate Report No. 928, 51st Cong., 1st Sess., is the product of the select committee on irrigation. For the purposes of the history of the Geological Survey there are four parts to this lengthy document: (1) the study of conditions in the arid West; (2) Powell's elaboration of his ideas and program; (3) his fatal dispute with the engineering profession; and (4) the majority and minority reports. The western legislators turned en masse against Powell in U. S., House Report No. 2407, 51st Cong., 1st Sess., and U. S., Senate Report No. 1466, 51st Cong., 1st Sess., both of which are hearings of committees on appropriations.

3. *Periodicals*

The American Journal of Science under the editorship of J. D. and E. S. Dana was a major source, both factual and dignified. When the two men opened the columns of their magazine to controversy, they were fair in the selection or expression of opinion. See J. D. Dana, "International Congress of Geology," *American Journal of Science,* Third Series, XXXVI (1888), 468-70; J. W. Powell, "Communication on the American Report of the International Congress of Geologists," *ibid.,* 476a-476e. On the number of phases in the Ice Age see G. F. Wright, "Unity of the Glacial Epoch," *ibid.,* XLIV (1892), 351-73; and T. C. Chamberlin, "The Diversity of the Glacial Period," *ibid.,* XLV (1893), 171-200. Objectivity is praiseworthy, but I found myself wishing that the reviews of Survey publications had been more critical or philosophical, after the manner of the British magazine *Nature. The American Geologist,* founded in 1888, operated on a much lower plane. Its prospectus (I, 1-3) naively announced "to all geologists of whatever school or party" that it would be conducted "above the influence of factions and of personal or local controversy."

The same prospectus expressed concern over the growing power of the national geological survey. Thereafter, many an issue of the new magazine proved conclusively that animus against the Survey was inspiring several of its editors. Despite the transparent prejudice, excellent materials sometimes appeared. The discussion on topographical mapping has merit, because officials of the Survey were allowed to reply: "The Topographical Map of the United States," *The American Geologist,* X (1892), 304-10; "The Topographical Work of the National Geological Survey," *ibid.,* XI (1893), 47-55; R. T. Hill, "The Topographical Work of the National Geological Survey," *ibid.,* 64-65; Henry Gannett, "The Topographical Work of the National Geological Survey," *ibid.,* 65-67, 127-28. See also J. C. Branner, "The Relations of the State and National Geological Survey to Each Other and to the Geologists of the Country," *ibid.,* VI (1890), 295-309. The weekly journal *Science* surveyed the social as well as the natural sciences, a dual operation which meant that one branch of knowledge could not receive extensive attention. Nevertheless, there are illuminating comments from time to time on the situation in Washington, which suggest the hand of Simon Newcomb, who was vice-president of the company that published the journal.

Occasionally, high caliber general magazines contributed to the literature of Survey history. E. L. Godkin gave space in *The Nation* to the controversy among the western surveys: "Who Shall Direct the National Surveys," *The Nation,* XVIII (1874), 328-29; "The War Department and the National Surveys," *ibid.,* 360-61; "Who Shall Direct Our National Surveys," *ibid.,* 361-62; "The National Surveys Again," *ibid.,* 377-78; *ibid.,* XXII (1876), 9; "Our Unavailable Public Lands," *ibid.,* XXVI (1876), 288-89; "The Proposed Reform in Our Land and Scientific Surveys," *ibid.,* XXVIII (1879), 27-29. In July and October 1875 the *North American Review* gave J. D. Whitney 90 pages for his "Geographical and Geological Surveys," *North American Review,* CXXI (1875), 37-85, 270-314.

J. W. Powell's articles on agrarian reform appeared as "The Irrigable Lands of the Arid Region," *Century Illustrated Monthly Magazine*, XXXIX (1890), 766-76; "The Non-Irrigable Lands of the Arid Region," *ibid.*, 915-22; "Institutions for the Arid Lands," *ibid.*, XL (1890), 111-16. The *Popular Science Monthly* introduced the participants in the dispute over the origin of man in North America: E. W. Claypole, "Prof. G. F. Wright and his Critics," *Popular Science Monthly*, XLII (1893), 764-81; G. F. Wright, "Evidences of Glacial Man in Ohio," *ibid.*, XLIII (1893), 29-39; J. W. Powell, "Are There Evidences of Man in the Glacial Gravels?" *ibid.*, 316-26.

4. *Science*

A major duty was to master the science of the Survey and place that science in historical perspective. Modern textbooks were studied, but the most help came from the *Professional Papers* of the Geological Survey, a series of this century. Geologists have gone over much of the territory which the Survey scientists covered between the Civil War and 1900, and usually these scholars have summarized, criticized, or referred in one way or another to the work of their earlier colleagues. On commemorative occasions scientists appraise the research of departing or past generations. In 1918 upon the one hundredth anniversary of its founding, the *American Journal of Science* published a series of articles on past science in the United States. Three of these articles were very helpful in the writing of Survey history: Charles Schuchert, "A Century of Geology: The Progress of Historical Geology in North America," *American Journal of Science*, Fourth Series, XLVI (1918), 45-103; H. E. Gregory, "A Century of Geology: Steps of Progress in the Interpretation of Land Forms," *ibid.*, 104-32; Joseph Barrell, "A Century of Geology: The Growth of Knowledge of Earth Structure," *ibid.*, 133-70. The anniversary number of the AJS was published separately as *A Century of Science in America, with Special Reference to the American*

Journal of Science, 1818-1918 (New Haven, 1918), and it
would have been convenient to cite this volume, except that
it is very scarce. Three other commemorative volumes, useful
to the historian, are: *Ore Deposits of the Western States,* ed.
by the committee on the Lindgren volume (New York, 1933);
Geology, 1888-1938: Fiftieth Anniversary Volume published
by the Geological Society of America (New York, 1941); and
A Century of Progress in the Natural Sciences, 1853-1953 published in celebration of the centennial of the California Academy of Sciences (San Francisco, 1955). Three standard histories
of geology and paleontology should be included: Frank Daw-
son, *The Birth and Development of the Geological Sciences*
(New York, 1938 and 1954), which is mostly about geology
and paleontology before Lyell; Karl von Zittel, *History of Geology and Paleontology* (London, 1901, and Weinheim, 1962),
which comes through the nineteenth century and has a European emphasis; and G. P. Merrill, *The First One Hundred
Years of American Geology* (New Haven, 1924, and New York,
1964), which has considerable information on the state and
western surveys. There is also, Richard Foster Flint, *Glacial
Geology and the Pleistocene Epoch* (New York, 1947). Three
biographies by scientists about scientists are: W. M. Davis,
Biographical Memoir: Grove Karl Gilbert, 1843-1918, Memoirs of the National Academy of Sciences, XXI (Washington,
1927); H. F. Osborn, *Cope: Master Naturalist* (New York,
1931); Charles Schuchert and Clara Mae LeVene, *O. C. Marsh,
Pioneer in Paleontology* (New Haven, 1940).

5. *King and Powell*

Clarence King Memoirs (New York, 1904), may serve as an
introduction to this unusual person. Despite inaccuracies, this
volume has all sorts of reminiscences to convey the high standing of King in the opinion of his distinguished friends. Francis
P. Farquhar's *Yosemite, the Big Trees, and the High Sierra: A
Selective Bibliography* (Berkeley, 1948), 33, 34, 47-53, is excel-

lent on King in California before his government service days. For a good account of the diamond hoax, see T. A. Rickard, *A History of American Mining* (New York, 1932), 380-96. David H. Dickason discusses King's esthetics in "Clarence King —Scientist and Art Amateur," *Art in America* (1944), 41-51, and *The Daring Young Men: The Story of the American Pre-Raphaelites* (Bloomington, 1953), 92-98. A passage in W. H. Jordy, *Henry Adams: Scientific Historian* (New Haven, 1952), 172-78, shows how King's catastrophism influenced Adams' pessimism; Jordy adds a bibliography on the uniformitarian-catastrophist controversy, 309-10. The book by Thurman Wilkins, *Clarence King: A Biography* (New York, 1958), is best on King's business and private affairs.

There are two biographies of the second director: William Culp Darrah, *Powell of the Colorado* (Princeton, 1951), and Wallace Stegner, *Beyond the Hundredth Meridian: John Wesley Powell and the Second Opening of the West* (Boston, 1954). Each has the story of the expedition down the Colorado River in 1869. Darrah discovered many day-to-day facts about his subject by interviewing descendants, acquaintances, and relatives of the Powell family. A strength of the Stegner volume is the regional setting which he provides for the Powell survey in the plateau country north of the Colorado River. For the pregovernment life of Powell, I recommend three articles by Mrs. M. D. Lincoln, "John Wesley Powell," *Open Court,* XVI (1902), 705-16, and *ibid.,* XVII (1903), 86-94, 163-74. These articles were written by a sentimental admirer, but she gives many a suggestive anecdote or fact about the youth, education, and early scientific activity of this remarkable man. William Culp Darrah has contributed a documentary collection to the *Utah Historical Quarterly,* XV (1947), on Powell's explorations down the Colorado River in 1869 and 1871. One important document is missing: a copy of the contract between the leader and three members of the first expedition, available in F. S. Dellenbaugh, *The Romance of the Colorado River*

. . . 3rd ed. (New York, 1909), 371. The land reforms of Powell for the arid West continue to attract attention. See, Walter Prescott Webb, *The Great Plains* (Boston, 1931), 419-22; James C. Malin, *The Grassland of North America: Prolegomena to its History* (Lawrence, Kansas, 1947), 202-207; Henry Nash Smith, *Virgin Land: The American West as Symbol and Myth* (Cambridge, 1950), 195-200; Wallace Stegner, *Beyond the Hundredth Meridian,* Chapters III, V, VI. Webb, Smith, and Stegner are laudatory; Malin is critical. If anyone wishes to follow the career of the restless second director into other fields of knowledge, I recommend the bibliography in the *Proceedings* of the Washington Academy of Sciences, V (1903), 131-87. Ralph Henry Gabriel in his *Course of American Democratic Thought: An Intellectual History since 1815* (New York, 1940), 168-72, demonstrates the primitive and popular nature of Powell's social thought.

6. *The Geological Survey*

Readers should know about previous history writing. In 1918, the Institute for Government Research began its *Service Monographs of the United States Government* with *The U. S. Geological Survey: its History, Activities and Organization.* This little book is a compendium of laws, statistics, facts, and bibliography. Because it is consulted and copied, I point to the gross error (page 4) of imputing lack of publications to Powell's Survey of the Rocky Mountain Region. More recently, there is the article by J. C. Rabbit and M. C. Rabbit, "The U. S. Geological Survey: 75 Years of Service to the Nation, 1879-1954," *Science,* 119 (May 28, 1954), 741-58, which can serve as an introduction to the modern Survey. A. Hunter Dupree writes about the Survey in Chapter X of his *Science in the Federal Government: A History of Policies and Activities to 1940* (Cambridge, 1957), Wallace Stegner, *Beyond the Hundredth Meridian,* 269-93, and William H. Goetzmann, *Exploration and Empire: The Explorer and the Scientist in the Winning of the American West* (New York, 1966), 577-601. The biographers of Powell and King have followed the account of the founding of the Survey in Henry Nash Smith, "Clarence King, John Wesley Powell, and the Establishment of the United States Geological Survey," *Mississippi Valley Historical Review*, XXXIV (1947-1948), 37-58. E. W. Sterling in "The Powell Irrigation Survey, 1888-1893," *ibid.*, XXVII (1940-1941), 421-34, contributes description and summary. *Great Surveys of the American West* (Norman, Okla., 1962), by Richard A. Bartlett has separate accounts of the Hayden, King, Powell, and Wheeler surveys, but gives only slight attention to systematic science. See also, William H. Goetzmann, "The Wheeler Surveys and the Decline of Army Exploration in the West," in *The American West: An Appraisal,* ed. Robert G. Feris (Santa Fé, 1963), 37-47.

INDEX

AAAS: urged Act of March 3, 1891, 164

Abbot, H. L.: consent to academy plan, 44

Abert, J. J.: compared to Powell, 216

Absaroka Range, Wyoming: as forest reserve, 155-56

Act of March 3, 1891: conservation clause in, 164; opportunity in for park, 164; and USGS, 221

Adams, Henry: eulogy of King, 70-71; reviewed Sheffield address, 88n

Adirondack Survey, 127

Agassiz, Alexander: acknowledged advice, 40n; philosophy of government science, 41, 134-35; member of Special Committee, 42; aid of to Herbert, 134-35; attacked USGS, 134-35; influence on Cleveland, 135; on Becker, 135; on Dutton trip, 135; skeptical of Chenoweth, 135; quoted, 207

Agassiz, Louis: Hayden compared to, 15

Agriculture Department: influenced by USGS, 216

Alabama geological survey, 118, 120

Alaska: USGS in, 218

Albuquerque, New Mexico: and topographical mapping, 177

Allen, J. B.: blamed Powell, 195; namecalling of, 199

Allen County, Kansas: poor mapping in, 103

Allison, W. B.: chairman, joint commission, 123, 143-44; praised Powell, 125, 170; on Herbert report, 140; fear of land speculation, 173; and irrigation amendment, 175-77; bewilderment of, 196; comment on Marsh, 209; heard from Osborn, 209; unenthusiastic about USGS, 209

American Falls, Montana: as reservoir site, 180

American geology: early research in, 1; independence established in, 1-2; western opportunities, 2; explanation of mountain building in, 32; movement toward uniformitarianism, 84, 87-88; progressive, 92; public science, 136

American Institute of Mining Engineers: and theory of ore formation, 225

American Society of Civil Engineers: urged topographic mapping, 102

Appalachian coalfields: location of USGS research, 116

Appalachian Mountains: state research on, 1; and uniformitarianism, 85-86; and topographical mapping, 95, 97; geological mapping in, 115-16

Arid lands. *See* Arid region; Irrigation survey

Arid region: definition of, 27; comment on, 47; irrigation sentiment in, 168-69; House hope for, 173-74; hydrographic basins in, 180; divided into districts, 180-82; and issue of artesian water, 182-84; and issue of public lands, 190-201

Arkansas geological survey: relations with USGS, 120, 221-22

Arkansas River, Colorado: gauging stations in, 178

Arkansas River Valley: and topographical mapping, 177

Army engineers. *See* U.S. Corps of Engineers

Artesian water: issue of, 182-84

Arthur, Chester: signed bill, 73

Asheville, North Carolina: and USGS research, 116

Aspen, Colorado: asked for USGS rescarch, 109; USGS at, 218

Atkins, J. D. C.: resolution of, 38; speech of, 47; support for USGS, 52-53; interest in mineral deposits, 65; amendments of, 66, 71-72; on states' rights, 68

Bache, A. D.: compared to Powell, 216

Baird, S. F.: opposed academy action, 39-40; approved academy plan, 44

head, Appalachian division, 116; on topographical maps, 185-86; lower salary of, 211; and the moon, 212-13; in water resources, 219

Gold gravels: USGS research in, 111-12

Goode, R. U.: topographer, 94

Gorman, A. P.: critic of Wolcott, 213

Government science: made acceptable, 5; praised, 10-11; as reform, 27, 28, 42, 43, 47, 48, 49, 180-82, 199; civilian-military rivalry in, 32-37, 40-41, 44-45, 47-48; patronage and, 37, 94, 130-31, 146n, 204, 207-208, 209-10, 220; changing position of, 38; laissez faire philosophy of, 41, 42, 43, 47, 49, 132-33, 134-35; utilitarian definition of, 42; economy demanded in, 68-69, 148n; centralizing trend of, 120, 121; principles of, 123; practical or theoretical, 136, 223-24; function and quality of, 185-89; attacked by Democrats, 206-210; Republicans defended, 207-208; misunderstanding of, 225-26. See also States' rights

Grand Canyon of the Colorado: explored, 2-3; research on, 21-22; origin of and erosion at, 77

Grand Canyon of the Yellowstone, 157

Grant, U.S.: signed park bill, 18; supported Survey West of One Hundredth Meridian, 33; on the military, and scientfic surveys, 34

Great Basin: location of Fortieth Parallel Exploration, 2, 5

Great Basin lunch mess: meaning of, 114

Great Falls, Montana: reservoir site, 179

"Great Unknown": term used by Powell, 21-22

Grinnell, G. B.: advocate of park, 161

Griswold, W. T.: work of praised, 102

Groff, L. A.: orders of, 192, 201; used Powell map, 195

Guyot, Arnold: support for Hayden, 54-55

Hagerman, J. J.: president, Pecos irrigation company, 198

Haggin and Carr: land company, 198

Hague, Arnold: assistant in Fortieth Parallel Exploration, 8, 12; geologist in USGS, 59; on methodology, 90-91; on Cleveland and science, 127; reaction to Herbert bill, 139; in charge, Yellowstone Park division, 151; park bill of, 155-56; new thinking of, 155, 156; visit to Cooke City, 158; feared army, 159; member, Boone and Crockett Club, 162; defeatism of, 163; used Act of March 3, 1891, 164; pleasure of, 165; no longer in Yellowstone, 167; on irrigation survey, 201; quoted, 206; on Cope-Marsh feud, 206n. See also Yellowstone National Park

Hague, James D.: studied Comstock Lode, 8-9

Hale, Eugene: national map challenged by, 124-25; fear of government involvement, 172; and public lands, 196

Hall, C. W.: in the USGS, 119

Harrison, Benjamin: on railroad promoters, 158; forest reserve proclaimed by, 164; and public lands, 193

Harvard College: support for Survey of Territories, 33

Haskell, D. D.: mocked scientists, 49; letter read by, 51

Hawkins, G. T.: topographer, 94

Hawley, J. B.: support for park, 162

Hay, Robert: critique of USGS maps, 103, 103n

Hayden, F. V.: joined Interior Department, 14; early life, 14n; personal research, 15-16, 18-19; led expedition into Yellowstone, 16; drew park boundary, 16-17;

163; approved compromise, 165; and mapping, 214

Manual of Geology: published by Dana, 1-2

Marcou, Jules: praise for Survey of Territories, 20; on USGS, 210n

Marsh, O. C.: vice-president, academy, 39; chairman, Special Committee, 40-41; accepted civilian control, 40-41; in Washington, 44; joined USGS, 82; studies of, 82, 83; New York *Times* on, 128; job of wanted by Cope, 132; accused of sinecure, 145; secretive, monopolistic, 205-206; unpopularity of, 206; feud with Cope, 206n; left USGS, 211; rejoined USGS, 221

Marvine, A. R.: work of, 18

Massachusetts, state of: mapping agreement with, 98, 99, 100

Massachusetts Institute of Technology: support for Survey of Territories, 33

Massachusetts state board of health: and USGS maps, 102

May, Daniel: contractor, 166

Meigs, M. C.: advocate of military, 41; consent to academy plan, 44

Mendenhall, Walter C.: director, 226; on research, 226

Merrill, W. E.: and western surveys, 46n

Miles City, Montana: approved compromise, 166

Milwaukee, Lake Shore, and Western Railroad: president of praised USGS, 115

Mineral Resources of the United States: USGS publication, 113

Mineral statistics: lack of, 65-66; USGS work in, 112-13

Minidoka Ferry, Montana: as reservoir site, 180

Mining industry: interest in geology, 2; petitioned for knowledge, 4; influence on USGS founding, 53; support for King, 55; philosophy of, 63-64; behind USGS expansion, 64-65; handicapped,

64-65; approved USGS, 109, 149; praise for Becker, 110

Minnesota geological survey: relations with USGS, 119

Missouri geological survey: cooperation with USGS, 118-19

Missouri River Valley: and artesian water, 183

Monopoly: Powell on, 194; in public lands, 198-99; and Colorado, 199; debated in House, 200-201

Montana legislature: support for railroad and mining, 153-54

Montana Mineral Railway Company: opposition to compromise, 166; true nature of, 166

Montana Territory: sentiment for railroad, 153-54

Moody, G. C.: advocate of artesian water, 183; complaint of, 184; blamed Powell, 195; anonymous letter read by, 196-97

Morgan, J. T.: joint commission member, 140; cosponsor of Herbert bill, 140; praise of Powell, 143; before joint commission, 143, 144, 145; namecalling of, 199

Mount Greylock, Massachusetts: Paleozoic and pre-Cambrian strata of, 80-81

Mountain building: King and complexity of, 14; new theory of by Gilbert, 32; as uniform process, 85-86

National Academy of Sciences: investigation by, 39; approval of Special Committee, 43-44; newspapers on, 45; rumors about, 128, 129, 130

National domain: location of the USGS, 54n; meaning of, 66

Natural Science: magazine, 213

Nature: magazine, 12-13

Naugatuck Valley, Connecticut: and USGS map, 102

Neale, A. T.: advocate of mapping, 99

INDEX